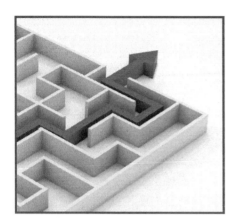

Medica...
Management
Tracer Workbook

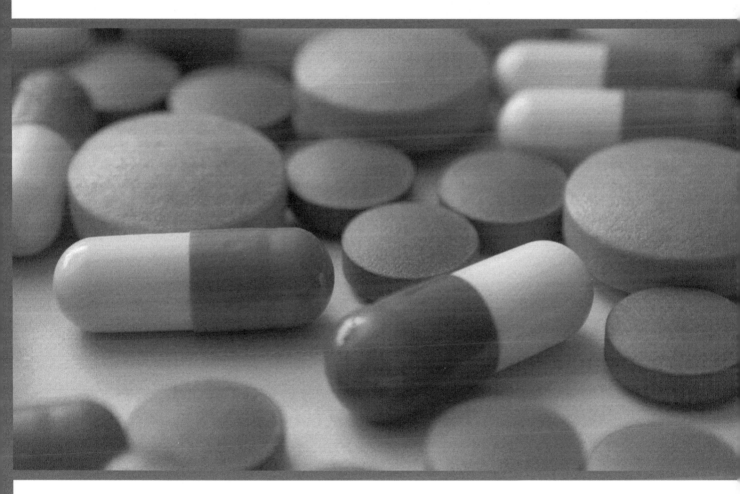

Joint Commission Resources

Joint Commission International

Senior Editor: Robert A. Porché, Jr.
Project Manager: Bridget Chambers
Manager, Publications: Lisa Abel
Associate Director, Production: Johanna Harris
Executive Director: Catherine Chopp Hinckley, Ph.D.

Joint Commission/Joint Commission Resources/Joint Commission International Reviewers: Mary Cesare-Murphy, Ph.D.; Kwong Ming Fock, M.B.B.S., M.Med., F.R.C.P., F.R.A.C.P., F.A.M.S.; Nancy L. Gorman, M.S., R.N., N.H.A.; Ann Jacobson, M.S.N., R.N., N.E.A.; Sherry Kaufield, M.A., F.A.C.H.E.; Michael Kulczycki, M.B.A.; Margherita C. Labson, R.N., M.S.H.S.A., C.C.M., C.P.H.Q., C.G.B.; Jeannell Mansur, R.Ph., Pharm.D., F.A.S.H.P.; Carol Mooney, R.N., M.S.N.; Derick P. Pasternak, M.D., M.B.A., F.A.C.P.E.; Mark G. Pelletier, R.N., M.S.; Kelly L. Podgorny, R.N., M.S., C.P.H.Q.; Mark E. Schario, M.S., R.N., F.A.C.H.E.

Joint Commission Resources Mission
The mission of Joint Commission Resources (JCR) is to continuously improve the safety and quality of health care in the United States and in the international community through the provision of education, publications, consultation, and evaluation services.

Joint Commission International
A division of Joint Commission Resources, Inc.
The mission of Joint Commission International (JCI) is to improve the safety and quality of care in the international community through the provision of education, publications, consultation, and evaluation services.

Joint Commission Resources educational programs and publications support, but are separate from, the accreditation activities of The Joint Commission. Attendees at Joint Commission Resources educational programs and purchasers of Joint Commission Resources publications receive no special consideration or treatment in, or confidential information about, the accreditation process.

The inclusion of an organization name, product, or service in a Joint Commission Resources publication should not be construed as an endorsement of such organization, product, or service, nor is failure to include an organization name, product, or service to be construed as disapproval.

Joint Commission Resources, Inc. (JCR), a not-for-profit affiliate of The Joint Commission, has been designated by The Joint Commission to publish publications and multimedia products. JCR reproduces and distributes these materials under license from The Joint Commission.

Printed in the U.S.A. 5 4 3 2 1

Requests for permission to make copies of any part of this work should be mailed to
Permissions Editor
Department of Publications
Joint Commission Resources
One Renaissance Boulevard
Oakbrook Terrace, Illinois 60181 U.S.A.
permissions@jcrinc.com

ISBN: 978-1-59940-609-1
Library of Congress Control Number: 2011925636

For more information about Joint Commission Resources, please visit http://www.jcrinc.com.

For more information about JCI, please visit http://www.jointcommissioninternational.org.

Table of Contents

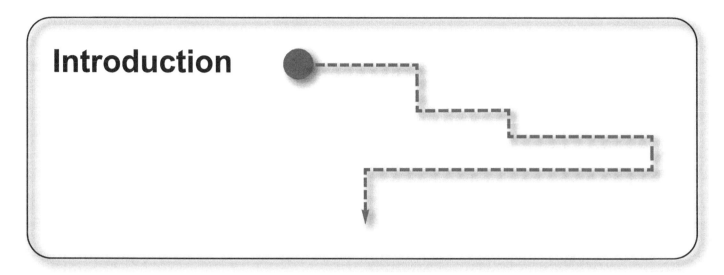

Introduction

Tracer methodology is an integral part of the on-site accreditation survey process used by The Joint Commission and Joint Commission International (JCI). Surveyors use tracers to evaluate the care of an individual or to evaluate a specific care process as part of a larger system. A surveyor reviews an individual's record and follows the specific care processes the individual experienced by observing and talking with staff members in areas where the individual received care. This methodology provides the surveyor with an opportunity to assess the organization's systems for providing care and services and its compliance with accreditation requirements. This book, part of a series that focuses on familiarizing health care staff with tracer methodology, can help an organization learn to conduct simulated—or mock—tracers that mimic actual tracers. The mock tracer is conducted by someone in the organization who performs the role of an actual surveyor.

Benefits of Understanding Tracers

Health care organizations that educate staff about tracers will have a better understanding of the overall survey process, especially since an on-site surveyor can typically devote up to 60% of his or her time conducting tracers. In addition, an organization that understands tracers can use mock tracers as a tool to assess its compliance with standards and make improvements before a surveyor arrives. For example, if an organization wants to analyze how well a specific aspect of a system on a specific unit functions—such as the security in the neonatal intensive care unit of a hospital—it can conduct a mock tracer of that system. Although its purpose would be to learn more about how systems function in that particular unit, a mock tracer

would also provide important information that could identify broader issues for improvement.

Types of Tracers

Surveyors currently conduct three types of tracers:

- *Individual:* An individual tracer follows the actual experience of an individual who received care, treatment, or services in a health care organization (that is, a patient, a resident, or an individual served). To select individuals to trace in U.S. health care organizations, surveyors take into account an organization's clinical/service groups (CSGs) and its top priority focus areas (PFAs) identified through the Joint Commission's Priority Focus Process. The CSGs categorize care recipients and selected services into distinct populations for which data can be collected. PFAs are processes, systems, or structures in a health care organization that significantly impact safety and/or the quality of care provided (*see* Appendix A). The organization's specific CSGs and PFAs inform the choice of what types of areas, units, services, departments, programs, or homes to visit initially to conduct an individual tracer; the CSGs, in turn, help the surveyor select an individual to trace. Although information from the Priority Focus Process may help surveyors select the first individuals and areas to trace, a surveyor may trace the experience of additional care recipients based on the initial findings during the on-site survey.

- *System based:* A surveyor may use a system-based tracer to analyze a high-risk process or system across an entire organization to evaluate how and how well that system functions. Currently, there are three topics explored during the on-site survey using the system tracer approach: medication management, infection control, and data management. To analyze a medication management or infection control system, a surveyor can follow an individual's actual care experience through the organization and assess how well that particular system functioned related to that individual's care. But to analyze a data management system, the surveyor conducts a group meeting session and focuses on assessing an organization's use of data in improving safety and quality of care. The goal of a data management system tracer is to learn about an organization's performance improvement process, including the organization, control, and use of data. There is no individual care recipient to follow; however, data from performance improvement are used and evaluated during the course of individual tracers throughout a survey. This book focuses on medication management system tracers.

- *Program specific:* A surveyor may use a program-specific tracer to analyze the unique characteristics and relevant issues of a specific type of organization. The goal of this type of tracer is to identify safety concerns in different levels and types of care. For example, a patient flow tracer is a program-specific tracer used in hospitals, whereas a continuity of care tracer is a program-specific tracer used in an ambulatory care organization.

A survey may also include an **environment of care** (EC) **tracer.** Like a system tracer, this type of tracer examines organizational systems and processes—in this case, systems related to the physical environment.

Second Generation Tracers

During any type of tracer, a surveyor may see something involving a high-risk area that requires a more in-depth look. At that point, the surveyor may decide to conduct a second generation tracer, which is a deep and detailed exploration of a particular area, process, or subject. These types of tracers are a natural evolution of the existing tracer process.

The following are high-risk topics in hospitals and critical access hospitals that surveyors might explore in more detail using a second generation tracer approach: cleaning, disinfection, and sterilization (CDS); patient flow across care continuum; contracted services; diagnostic imaging; and ongoing professional practice evaluation (OPPE)/focused professional practice evaluation (FPPE).

Tracers Used Internationally

Tracer methodology is being used to assess health care organizations beyond the United States. Health care organizations that undergo JCI accreditation also experience tracer methodology when surveyors visit their facilities. The concept is essentially the same for both domestic and international organizations; however, there are slight differences. Whereas U.S. surveyors use such elements as PFAs and CSGs to select care recipients to trace, these criteria do not apply to international surveys. JCI surveyors use information provided in the organization's accreditation survey application to select tracer subjects from an active care recipient list. Subjects typically selected are those who have received multiple or complex services because they, most likely, have had more contact with various departments of the organization, providing a greater opportunity for the surveyor to assess how systems work in the organization. Furthermore, program-specific tracers are done as part of "undetermined survey activity" appropriate to an organization, as defined in the *JCI Survey Process Guide*. Also, international organizations refer to the EC tracers as "facility management and safety" tracers and to data management system tracers as "improvement in quality and patient safety" tracers.

Conducting Mock Tracers

The best way to understand all types of tracers is through practice—that is, through conducting mock tracers. This involves developing some basic skills, such as learning how to ask good questions. An actual tracer is not performed by one person in isolation. It involves talking with multiple staff members and, in the case of individual tracers and some system tracers, the care recipient and even family members (if possible) to learn details about an individual's health care experience or how a particular system functions in an organization. All important details about the individual's care or the system's function can be explored by asking simple questions in succession. And how a question is asked is particularly important. A surveyor poses questions in a manner that encourages the staff member or care recipient to share as much information as possible. Observation of the surroundings or attention to how a respondent answers one question can lead to other related issues and can trigger additional questions.

Skills in analysis and organization are also involved, particularly in planning a mock tracer, and of course, analysis is necessary to evaluate and prioritize the results of a mock tracer. Similar skills are involved in the reporting of the results and in the follow-up on any consequent plans for improvement based on the results. Often, an organization will institute a mock tracer program that will train participants for optimum outcomes to these practice tracers. The benefits that result from mock tracers support and enhance the continuation of such teams.

How to Use This Book

Medication Management Tracer Workbook is designed to help staff members in all health care settings better understand how medication management system tracers work and how to conduct mock tracers:

- "How to Conduct a Mock Tracer" follows this Introduction. It provides step-by-step instruction on performing a mock tracer.

- The Overview that follows "How to Conduct a Mock Tracer" goes into further detail about system tracers, and in particular, medication management system tracers.

- Each section of this workbook includes example tracers, called scenarios, that are specific to a type of health care setting (such as home care and behavioral health care).

- Each scenario is preceded by a list of the PFAs that emerge during the scenario. For scenarios in an international setting, this summary also explains the criteria for the tracer subject selection. Then, a narrative describes how a surveyor might analyze a particular medication management system.

- Sample tracer questions follow each scenario. They show the types of questions a surveyor might ask staff members or other individuals for the specific scenario. These questions are keyed to the narrative to show how and when they might occur during the scenario.

- Each section also includes an example of a tracer worksheet that utilizes the sample tracer questions from one scenario and shows how the worksheet might be completed during mock tracer activities.

- Appendixes describe the PFAs, provide forms that are helpful in developing a mock tracer program, and include a listing of domestic and international patient safety goals and medication management standards.

Terms Used in This Book

This publication is divided into sections that are health care–setting specific, so each section will use terminology appropriate for its setting. For example, *patient* will be used for hospital, ambulatory care, and home care settings; *individual* will be used for behavioral care settings; and resident will be used for long term care settings. The term *health care* in this workbook refers to all types of care, treatment, or services provided within the spectrum of the health care field, including physical, medical, and behavioral health care.

Acknowledgments

Joint Commission Resources (JCR) is grateful to the multiple reviewers and content experts for their feedback to ensure that the overall content about tracers is accurate and relevant to the numerous health care settings. A special thank you is extended to these contributors: Kenneth G. Hermann, M.H.A., Pharm.D., F.A.C.H.E., Medication Management Consultant; Jeannell M. Mansur, R.Ph., Pharm.D., F.A.S.H.P, Practice Leader, Joint Commission Resources; Carol Ptasinski, R.N., M.S.N., M.B.A., Field Director, Surveyor Management and Development, Accreditation and Certification Operations, The Joint Commission; Steve Olsen, Pharm.D., Medication Management Consultant; Derick P. Pasternak, M.D, M.B.A., F.A.C.P.E., Senior Consultant, Joint Commission International; Mark E. Schario, M.S., R.N., F.A.C.H.E., Field Director, Surveyor Management and Development, Accreditation and Certification Operations, The Joint Commission; and Genie Skypek, Surveyor, Behavioral Health Care Accreditation Program, The Joint Commission. We also extend our gratitude to writer Janet McIntyre for her dedication and patience in writing this book.

In addition, we are grateful to our Joint Commission reviewers
(*see* page ii) for their thorough and timely input.

How to Conduct a Mock Tracer

The main activity during a Joint Commission or Joint Commission International (JCI) survey of any type of health care organization is the tracer (*see* the sidebar "Tracers at a Glance," at right). A **mock tracer** is a practice tracer meant to simulate an actual tracer. During a mock tracer, one or more people may play the role of a surveyor. Some organizations develop teams of such "surveyors" and repeatedly conduct mock tracers as part of an ongoing mock tracer program.

Mock tracers are done for several reasons:
- To evaluate the effectiveness of an organization's policies and procedures
- To engage staff in looking for opportunities to improve processes
- To be certain the organization has addressed compliance issues and is ready for survey at any time

What follows is a 10-step primer for how to conduct a mock tracer. It addresses the process in four phases:
- Planning and preparing for the mock tracer
- Conducting and evaluating the mock tracer
- Analyzing and reporting the results of the mock tracer
- Applying the results of the mock tracer

Each step within these phases includes suggested approaches and activities. You might want to use the "Mock Tracer Checklist and Time Line" on page 7 to guide you through the phases. The primer also explains how to use the scenarios, sample worksheets, and appendixes in this workbook to conduct mock tracers. Note that the primer can be modified to suit any health care organization.

Tracers at a Glance

Duration: A Joint Commission individual tracer (*see* "Individual tracers" on page 6) is scheduled to take 60 to 90 minutes but may take several hours. During a typical three-day survey, a surveyor or survey team may complete several tracers; during a single-day survey, it may be possible to complete only one or two tracers. Tracers constitute about 60% of the survey.

Survey team: A typical Joint Commission survey team includes one or more surveyors with expertise in the organization's accreditation program. For domestic (not international) hospitals and critical access hospitals, a *Life Safety Code*®* Specialist is also part of the team. A team leader is assigned for any survey with more than one surveyor. A surveyor typically conducts a tracer on his or her own and later meets up with the rest of the team to discuss findings.

Tracer activity: During tracer activity, surveyors evaluate the following:
- Compliance with Joint Commission standards and National Patient Safety Goals and, **JCI** for international organizations, JCI standards and International Patient Safety Goals
- Consistent adherence to organization policy and consistent implementation of procedures
- Communication within and between departments/programs/services
- Staff competency for assignments and workload capacity

(continued)

---

* Life Safety Code *is a registered trademark of the National Fire Protection Association, Quincy, MA.*

Tracers at a Glance (continued)

- The physical environment as it relates to the safety of care recipients, visitors, and staff

Range of observation: During a tracer, the surveyor(s) may visit (and revisit) any department/program/service or area of the organization related to the care of the individual served or to the functioning of a system.

Individual tracers: Individual (patient) tracer activity usually includes observing care, treatment, or services and associated processes; reviewing open or closed medical records related to the care recipient's care, treatment, or services and other processes, as well as examining other documents; and interviewing staff as well as care recipients and their families. An individual tracer follows (traces) one care recipient throughout his or her care in the organization.

System tracers: A system tracer relates to a high-risk system or the processes that make up that system in an organization. Currently, three topics are explored during the on-site survey using the system tracer approach: medication management, infection control, and data management. The data management system tracer is the only tracer that is routinely scheduled to occur on regular surveys for most organizations; it may include evaluation of data for medication management and infection control, as well. Other system tracers take place based on the duration of the on-site survey; the type of care, treatment, or services provided by the organization; and the organization's accreditation history. Lab accreditation programs do not have system tracers. **JCI** In international organizations, data system tracers are called "improvement in quality and patient safety" tracers and are not individual based.

Program-specific tracers: These are tracers that focus on topics pertinent to a particular accreditation program and the associated care, treatment, or service processes. These processes are explored through the experience of a care recipient who has needed or may have a future need for the organization's care, treatment, or services. Examples include patient flow in a hospital or suicide prevention at a residential program. Lab accreditation programs do not have program-specific tracers.

Environment of care tracers: Although the environment of care (EC) tracer is not one of the defined Joint Commission system tracers, it is similar to those types of tracers. Like system tracers, EC tracers examine organization systems and processes—in this case, systems related to the physical environment, emergency management, and life safety. Also, like system tracers, an EC tracer is often triggered by something observed during an individual tracer, as surveyors notice environmental-, emergency management–, and life safety–based risks associated with a care recipient and the staff providing care, treatment, or services to that person. A surveyor may also be assigned to do an EC tracer as part of a comprehensive survey process. Note that EC tracers are performed only in facility-based accreditation programs and do not apply to community-based programs and services, such as those provided by some behavioral health care accreditation programs. **JCI** For international organizations, EC is referred to as "facility management and safety."

Second generation tracers: A surveyor may see something during a tracer involving select high-risk areas that requires a more in-depth look. At that point, the surveyor may decide to conduct a second generation tracer, which is a deep and detailed exploration of a particular area, process, or subject.

Planning and Preparing for the Mock Tracer

Step 1: Establish a Schedule for the Mock Tracer

Careful planning is necessary for any successful activity, including a mock tracer. Consider the following when establishing a schedule for mock tracers in your organization:

- *Schedule by phase:* Allow adequate time for each phase of a mock tracer. The focus of each phase outlined in this primer is shown in the checklist "Mock Tracer Checklist and Time Line" (see page 7) with suggested time frames, some of which may overlap. Suggested approaches and activities for each phase comprise the remainder of this primer.

Mock Tracer Checklist and Timeline

✔ Planning and Preparing for the Mock Tracer	
Step 1: Establish a Schedule for the Mock Tracer	Month 1
Step 2: Determine the Scope of the Mock Tracer	Month 1
Step 3: Choose Those Playing the Roles of Surveyors	Month 1
Step 4: Train Those Playing the Roles of Surveyors	Months 1 and 2
✔ Conducting and Evaluating the Mock Tracer	
Step 5: Assign the Mock Tracer	Month 2
Step 6: Conduct the Mock Tracer	Month 3
Step 7: Debrief About the Mock Tracer Process	Month 3
✔ Analyzing and Reporting the Results of the Mock Tracer	
Step 8: Organize and Analyze the Results of the Mock Tracer	Month 4
Step 9: Report the Results of the Mock Tracer	Month 4
✔ Applying the Results of the Mock Tracer	
Step 10: Develop and Implement Improvement Plans	Months 5–7

Note: *To follow up on findings and sustain the gains, periodically repeat mock tracers on the same subjects.*

- *Make it part of your regular PI program:* Make mock tracers part of your ongoing performance improvement (PI) program. Schedule mock tracers for different departments/ programs/services several times a year.

- *Share the plan with everyone:* Let everyone in your organization know about the mock tracers being planned. No set dates need to be given if the mock tracers are to be unannounced, but communication about planned and ongoing mock tracers is necessary for recruitment of those who will play the roles of surveyors and for cooperation from all departments/programs/services.

- *Understand the Joint Commission survey agenda:* A mock tracer typically simulates only the tracer portion of a survey, which constitutes the foundation of the survey. By understanding the survey activities, however, those who are playing the roles of surveyors can better simulate tracers to help your organization prepare for a survey. Joint Commission surveys follow a tight agenda. Check the *Survey Activity Guide* (*SAG*) for your accreditation program(s). The guide outlines what happens in each survey activity. All accreditation program *SAG*s are posted on the Web site for The Joint Commission. They are also available on your *Joint Commission Connect*™ extranet site if yours is an accredited health care organization or an organization seeking Joint Commission accreditation. **JCI** International organizations should consult the *International Survey Process Guide* (SPG), which is sent to applicants seeking international accreditation and is also available to order on the JCI Web site.

- *Relate it to the date of the last survey:* Joint Commission surveys are typically conducted on a regular, triennial basis. For most accredited organizations, the survey will occur within 18 to 36 months after an organization's last survey, although laboratory surveys and certification program reviews are on a two-year cycle. With the exception of critical access hospitals and office-based surgery practices, organizations accredited by The Joint Commission must conduct Periodic Performance Reviews (PPRs) between full surveys. The PPR is a management tool that helps the organization incorporate Joint Commission standards as part of routine operations and ongoing quality improvement efforts, supporting a continuous accreditation process. A mock tracer can help by giving the organization more insight into compliance issues. Conducting the mock tracer before a survey date allows time to address compliance issues prior to the PPR deadline; conducting a mock tracer shortly after the last survey is helpful for assessing compliance with problems highlighted in that recent survey. Note that the PPR is not applicable to the Medicare/Medicaid certification–based long term care accreditation program. **JCI** For international organizations, the survey will occur within 45 days before or after the accreditation expiration date. International certification programs are on a three-year review cycle. Also, although international organizations are not required to complete PPRs, JCI recommends that organizations do a self-assessment of compliance between surveys. (International certification programs have a required intra-cycle review process.)

Step 2: Determine the Scope of the Mock Tracer

Assess your organization to determine where to focus attention. By listing problems and issues in your organization, the scope of the mock tracer—whether comprehensive or limited—will become clear. One or more of the following approaches may be used to determine a mock tracer's scope:

- *Imitate the Priority Focus Process:* The Priority Focus Process (PFP) provides a summary of the top clinical/service groups (CSGs) and priority focus areas (PFAs) for an organization. The CSGs categorize care recipients and/or services into distinct populations for which data can be collected. The PFAs are processes, systems, or structures in a health care organization that significantly impact safety and/or the quality of care provided (*see* Appendix A). The PFP is accessible on the *Joint Commission Connect* site for domestic organizations and provides organizations with the same information that surveyors have when they conduct on-site evaluations. Address all or some of the areas generated in that report. **JCI** International organizations do not have PFPs; however, it may be helpful and important to look at your last survey results and target areas of greatest concern.

- *Reflect your organization:* Start with your organization's mission, scope of care, range of treatment or services, and population(s) served. Choose representative tracers that support and define your organization. You might want to use an assessment tool, such as the Comprehensive Originization Assessment, to gather this data. (*See* Appendix C).

- *Target the top compliance issues:* Review the Joint Commission's top 10 standards compliance issues, published regularly in *The Joint Commission Perspectives®* (available for subscription and provided free to all accredited organizations). Also check any issues highlighted in *Sentinel Event Alerts*, which are available on the Joint Commission Web site, at http://www.jointcommission.org/sentinel_event.aspx. Address compliance issues that are also problem prone in your organization. Be especially mindful to note if any of these top compliance issues have been noted in current or past PPRs. **JCI** International organizations can request top compliance issues from this address: JCIAccreditation@jcrinc.com.

- *Review what is new:* Address any new Joint Commission or JCI standards that relate to your organization. New standards and requirements are highlighted in the binder version (although not in the spiral-bound book version) of the most recent update of the *Comprehensive Accreditation Manual* for your program. Also focus on any new equipment or new programs or services in your organization. Consider mock tracers that will allow opportunities to evaluate newly implemented or controversial or problematic organization policies and procedures and how consistently they are being followed.

- *Start with the subject:* Look at typical tracers from any past surveys and choose several common or relevant examples for the types of tracers defined in the Introduction to this workbook. Or, if your organization has never had a survey, consider the guidelines described in the sidebar "Choosing Tracer Subjects" on pages 9–10.

- *Cover the highs and lows:* Focus on high-volume/high-risk and low-volume/high-risk areas and activities. Ask questions about demographics for those areas or activities to help determine whether care, treatment, or services are targeted to a particular age group or diagnostic/condition category. Then pick corresponding tracer subjects.

- *Target time-sensitive tasks:* Look at time-sensitive tasks, such frequency of staff performance evaluations, critical result reporting, and the signing, dating, and timing of physician orders, including whether they are present and complete. These are often challenging compliance areas.

- *Examine vulnerable population(s):* Review the risks in serving particularly vulnerable, fragile, or unstable populations in your organization. Select tracer subjects (care recipients, systems, or processes) that might reveal possible failing outcomes. Address related processes of care, treatment, or services that are investigational, new, or otherwise especially risky.

Step 3: Choose Those Playing the Roles of Surveyors

If your goal is to conduct more than one mock tracer, either concurrently or sequentially, you will want to develop a mock tracer team. Careful selection of those playing the roles of surveyors is critical. A general guide for a mock tracer team is to follow the number and configuration of your last Joint Commission or JCI survey team (*see* the sidebar "Tracers at a Glance" on page 5). However, you might want to involve more people or have multiple mock tracer teams; try to allow as many people as possible to be exposed to the tracer process and to learn more about the surveyors' angle on the process. If your organization has not had a survey yet, aim for five to eight team members, or select one team member for each department/program/service in your organization plus one for each type of system tracer and one for the EC. Consider the following when choosing those who will play the roles of surveyors:

- *Include administrators:* Administrators, managers, and other leadership should be not only supportive of mock tracers but also involved. Include at least one administrator or manager on the team. Include executive-level leaders in the early stages to provide input and model team leadership. Also, staff may need time off from their regular duties to participate in various phases of a mock tracer, so team members should be sure to get the approval of their managers.

- *Select quality-focused communicators:* Sharp, focused professionals with excellent communication skills are needed to play the roles of surveyors. Recruit people who are observant, detail oriented, and committed to quality and professionalism. Those playing the roles of surveyors should be articulate, polite, personable, and able to write clearly and succinctly. They should be comfortable talking to frontline staff, administrators, and care recipients and families.

- *Draw from committees:* Often the best choices for those who will play the roles of surveyors have already been identified and serve on various committees in your organization. Draw from committee members to find top-notch candidates.

Choosing Tracer Subjects

Individual tracers: For individual mock tracers, adopt the way actual surveyors choose care recipients. In U.S. health care organizations, select them based on criteria such as (1) whether they are from the top CSGs in the PFP; (2) whether their experience of care, treatment, or services allows the surveyor to access as many areas of the organization as possible; (3) whether they qualify under the criteria for any accreditation program–specific tracer topic areas; or (4) whether they move between and receive care, treatment, or services in multiple programs, sites, or levels of care within your organization. Also, consider tracing care recipients who have been recently admitted or who are due for discharge. **JCI** In international organizations, use information provided in your organization's accreditation survey application to select tracer care recipients from an active list that shows who has received multiple or complex services.

System tracers: Care recipients selected for tracing a system typically reflect those who present opportunities to explore both the routine processes and potential challenges to the system. For example, to evaluate medication management systems, select care recipients who have complex medication regimens, who are receiving high-alert medications, or who have had an adverse drug reaction. To evaluate infection control, select someone who is isolated or who is under contact precautions due to an existing infection or compromised immunity. These same care recipients could be the subjects for data management system tracers, as each might be included in performance measurement activities such as infection control surveillance or adverse drug-reaction monitoring data. **JCI** In international organizations, data system tracers are called "improvement in quality and patient safety" tracers and are not individual based.

Program-specific tracers: The focus for these tracers may include programs such as foster care, patient flow, continuity of care, fall reduction, and

(continued)

Choosing Tracer Subjects (continued)

suicide prevention. For example, to evaluate a falls reduction program in a long term care facility, you would select a resident identified as being at risk for falls to trace components of the program, such as care recipient education, risk assessment, and falls data.

Environment of care tracers: Subjects for an EC mock tracer may include systems and processes for safety, security, hazardous materials and waste, fire safety, utilities, and medical equipment. For example, an EC mock tracer might examine the security in the neonatal intensive care unit, the safety of hazardous materials that enter through the loading dock, or the installation of and maintenance for new medical equipment. Be sure also to include emergency management and life safety issues as topics for mock tracers. **JCI** In international organizations, EC is referred to as "facility management and safety."

Second generation tracers: Subjects for second generation tracers grow naturally out of tracers involving high-risk areas because this type of tracer is a deeper and more detailed exploration of the tracer subject. Areas subject to second generation tracers include cleaning, disinfection, and sterilization (CDS); patient flow across care continuum; contracted services; diagnostic imaging; and ongoing professional practice evaluation (OPPE)/focused professional practice evaluation (FPPE).

- *Don't forget physicians:* Because they are a critical part of any health care organization, physicians should be involved in mock tracers—and not always just as interview subjects. Recruit physicians to perform the roles of surveyors. This angle of participation will not only allow them to *apply* their expertise and experience but will also allow them to *add* to that expertise and experience.

- *Draft from HR, IM, and other departments or services:* Those playing the roles of surveyors may also be drafted from among the staff and managers of nonclinical departments, including human resources (HR) and information management (IM). Housekeeping and maintenance staff are

often valuable as "surveyors" for their unique perspective of daily operations.

Step 4: Train Those Playing the Roles of Surveyors

All staff trained to portray surveyors need to have both an overview and more detailed knowledge of tracers as part of their training. Even those who have been through a survey need training to play the role of a surveyor. Those who will be acting as surveyors should do the following as part of their training:

- *Get an overview:* Take some time to learn the basics of tracers. The Introduction to this workbook provides a good overview. As a next step, read the *Survey Activity Guide* for your program, which is posted on the Web site for The Joint Commission and on *Joint Commission Connect*. The guide explains what surveyors do in each part of the different types of tracers. **JCI** The JCI *Survey Process Guides* are provided to international organizations applying for accreditation and are also for sale on the JCI Web site.

- *Learn the standards:* Challenging as it may be, it is essential that those who are playing surveyors become familiar with current Joint Commission requirements related to the targeted tracer. They must gain a solid understanding of the related standards, National Patient Safety Goals, and Accreditation Participation Requirements. To learn about changes and updates to Joint Commission standards and how to interpret and apply them, they should read the monthly newsletter *Joint Commission Perspectives* (available for subscription and provided free to all domestic accredited organizations). Be particularly careful to give those who are playing surveyors sufficient time to learn the standards for the department or area in which they will conduct a mock tracer. At least one month is advised (*see* the sidebar "Mock Tracer Checklist and Time Line" on page 7). **JCI** International organizations should be familiar with JCI standards and International Patient Safety Goals, as outlined in the current relevant JCI accreditation manual. Updates, tips, and more are provided free via the online periodical *JCInsight*.

- *Welcome experience:* Staff and leaders who have been through a tracer can be valuable resources. Invite them to speak to the tracer team about their experiences with tracers and with surveys in general.

- *Examine closed medical records:* Closed medical records are an excellent practice tool for individual tracers and individual-based system tracers. Examine closed (but recent) records and then brainstorm the types of observations, document review, and questions that a surveyor might use to trace the subject of the record.

- *Study mock tracer scenarios:* Tracer scenarios, like those in this workbook, will help familiarize team members with the general flow of a tracer as well as the specific and unique nature of most tracers. The questions that follow each tracer scenario in this workbook can be used to populate a form for a mock tracer on a similar subject in your organization (*see* Appendix B). The sample tracer worksheet at the end of each section in this workbook provides a model for how someone playing the role of a surveyor might complete a worksheet based on such questions. **JCI** Note that scenarios with international content appear in the final section of the workbook, but issues addressed in scenarios for domestic settings may be transferable to international settings.

- *Practice interviewing:* Since a large part of a tracer is spent in conversation, people who are filling the roles of surveyors should practice interviewing each other. Although these people should already be good communicators, a review of common interview techniques may be helpful (*see* the sidebar "Interviewing Techniques" at right).

Conducting and Evaluating the Mock Tracer

Step 5: Assign the Mock Tracer

A mock tracer team may have one member play the roles of surveyor in a specific mock tracer, or the team members may take turns playing the role during the tracer. With repeated mock tracers, every team member should have the opportunity to play a surveyor. Consider these options when assigning role-playing surveyors to mock tracers:

- *Match the expert to the subject:* Match a "surveyor" who is an expert in a department/program/service to a mock tracer for a similar department/program/service— but for objectivity, do not assign them to the same specific department/program/service in which they work.

- *Mismatch the expert to the subject:* Match a "surveyor" to a department/program/service that is new to him or her. This may enhance the objective perspective. Of course, that person will have to prepare in advance to become familiar with the requirements for that new department/program/service.

Interviewing Techniques

- Take your time. Speak slowly and carefully.
- To help set the interview subject at ease, try mirroring: Adjust your volume, tone, and pace to match those of the person to whom you are speaking. (If the subject is nervous or defensive, however, use a quiet and calm approach to encourage that person to match your example.)
- Use "I" statements ("I think," "I see") to avoid appearing to challenge or blame the interview subject.
- Ask open-ended questions (to avoid "yes/no" answers).
- Pause before responding to a subject's answer to wait for more information.
- Listen attentively, gesturing to show you understand.
- Listen actively, restating the subject's words as necessary for clarification.
- Manage your reactions to difficult situations and avoid using a confrontational tone, even if your subject sets such a tone. Take a deep breath and wait at least three seconds before responding.
- Always thank your interview subject for his or her time and information.

- *Pair up or monitor:* Pair "surveyors" so they can learn from and support each other, or allow one "surveyor" to follow and monitor the other for additional experience. One of those in the pair might be the mock tracer team leader.

Step 6: Conduct the Mock Tracer

All departments/programs/services in your organization should already have been notified about the possibility of staff conducting mock tracers. Unless mock tracers are announced, however, there is no need to notify interview subjects when the tracer is scheduled to occur. During the mock tracer, team members should do the following:

- *Collect data:* Like real surveyors, those playing the roles of surveyors must collect data that help to establish whether your organization is in compliance with applicable accreditation requirements. They should do this by taking notes on their observations, conversations, and review of documents. Notes may be entered on an electronic form (using a laptop computer) or on a paper form.

- *Be methodical and detail oriented:* To help establish and simulate an actual tracer, those portraying surveyors should strive to be as methodical and detail oriented as actual surveyors. The following techniques may be useful:
  - ○ Map a route through the mock tracer, showing who will be interviewed in each area. It is helpful to interview the person who actually performed the function targeted by the tracer, but any person who performs the same function can be interviewed.

  - ○ Identify who will be interviewed in each area, using specific names (if staffing schedules are available) or general staff titles. For example, if you have singled out a particular care recipient to trace, identify which staff members cared for that care recipient. Of course, this may not be possible to do because staff to be interviewed may depend on what is found in the targeted area, where the care recipient travels within the organization, and what procedures are performed.

  - ○ Note the approximate amount of time to be spent in each department/program/service. That will help keep the tracer on schedule. Notwithstanding any tentative scheduling of the tracer, however, you may uncover unexpected findings that will necessitate either spending more time in a particular location or going to locations that were unforeseen at the time the tracer started. Flexibility is a key attribute of a good surveyor doing tracers.

  - ○ Take notes on a form, worksheet, or chart developed by the team for the purpose of the mock tracer. (The mock tracer worksheet form in Appendix B can be used for this purpose.)

  - ○ Surveyors are directed to be observant about EC issues. Some EC issues may be photographed for the record, provided that no care recipients are included in the photos.

- *Share the purpose:* Whenever possible, remind tracer interview subjects of the purpose of tracers and mock tracers: to learn how well a process or system is functioning (not to punish a particular staff member or department/program/service).

- *Maintain focus:* Keep the process on track and continually make connections to the broader issues affecting care recipient safety and delivery of care, treatment, or services.

- *Be flexible and productive:* If a person playing the role of a surveyor arrives in an area and has to wait for a particular interview subject, that time can be filled productively by interviewing other staff and making relevant observations and notes. If more than one mock tracer is scheduled for the same day—as in a real survey—"surveyors" may cross paths in an area. One "surveyor" should leave and return at a later time.

- *Address tracer problems:* Be prepared to identify and address any problems with the mock tracer process encountered during the mock tracer, including practical arrangements (such as the logistics of finding appropriate staff), department/program/service cooperation, team dynamics, and staying on schedule. Decide in advance whether to address such problems in an ad hoc fashion (as they are encountered) or as part of a debriefing after the mock tracer to prepare for subsequent mock tracers.

Step 7: Debrief About the Mock Tracer Process

After each mock tracer, and particularly after the first few, meet as a team as soon as possible to evaluate and document how it went. (Note: This debriefing session should focus on the mock tracer process, not what the mock tracer revealed about your organization's problems or issues. That will be done in Step 8: "Organize and Analyze the Results of the Mock Tracer"; *see* below.) You may choose to use one of the following approaches:

- *Hold an open forum:* An open forum should allow all team members to discuss anything about the tracer, such as methods, logistics, and conflict resolution. For a broader perspective, invite interview subjects from the mock tracer to participate.

- *Let each member present:* In a direct, focused approach, team members can present their feedback to the rest of the team, one at a time. Each person playing the role of a surveyor can be given a set amount of time to present, with questions to follow at the end of each presentation.

- *Fill out a feedback form:* Team members and mock tracer participants can complete a feedback form in which they record their impressions of the mock tracer and suggestions for improvement of the process. These can be vetted and then discussed at the next team meeting to plan for the next mock tracer.

Analyzing and Reporting the Results of the Mock Tracer

Step 8: Organize and Analyze the Results of the Mock Tracer

Conducting a mock tracer is not enough; the information gained from it must be organized and analyzed. The problems and issues revealed in the mock tracer must be reviewed, ranked, and prioritized. You might want to use one or more of the following suggested methods to do this:

- *File the forms:* If the mock tracer team used forms—either electronic or paper (such as the form in Appendix B), those can be categorized for review. The forms might be categorized by types of problems/issues or by department/program/service.

- *Preview the data:* Those who played the roles of surveyors should be the first to review the data (notes) they collected during the mock tracer. They should check for and correct errors in the recording of information and highlight what they consider to be issues of special concern.

- *Rank and prioritize the problems:* The team, led by the team leader, must carefully evaluate all of the team's data. Critical issues or trends can be identified and then ranked by severity/urgency with regard to threats to life or safety, standards noncompliance, and violations of other policies. Prioritizing is the next step and will require considerations such as the following:
  - What is the threat to health or safety? What is the degree of threat posed by the problem—immediate, possible, or remote?

  - What is the compliance level? Is the problem completely out of compliance? That is, does the problem relate to a standard that always requires full compliance (that is, Category A standards) or one for which you may be scored partially compliant or insufficiently compliant (that is, Category C standards)?

  - What resources are required? How much staff time and resources will likely be needed to correct the problem? Depending on the threat to health or safety and compliance level, there may be a time limit imposed on how soon the problem must be corrected (for example, immediately or within 45 or 60 days).

Step 9: Report the Results of the Mock Tracer

An organization's reaction to a mock tracer will depend largely on the results of the mock tracer, including how—and how well—the results are reported. In all reports, it is important to avoid having the tracer appear punitive or like an inspection, so do not include staff names or other identifying information. Following are several ways to report results effectively:

- *Publish a formal report:* Compile all documents and carefully edit them. Determine which documents most clearly summarize the issues. Submit a copy of the report to the appropriate leadership.

- *Present as a panel:* Invite leadership to a panel presentation in which team members present the results of the tracer—by department/program/service or by other arrangement (for example, problems with staffing, infection control, handoff communication, or transitions in care, treatment, or services).

- *Call a conference:* Set up an internal conference event in which you present the results. They could be presented on paper, delivered by speakers from a podium, and/or delivered using audiovisual formats. Invite leadership and everyone who participated in the mock tracer. Keep the conference brief (no more than two hours), being considerate of attendees' time. Make the content easier to digest by color-coding the level of priority and using other keys to signal the types of problems and their severity. Open up the conference to feedback with breakout brainstorming sessions on how to address the problems.

- *Post for feedback:* Post the results on a secure organization intranet and ask for feedback and suggestions from participants and others in your organization. A bulletin board in the lunchroom works, too. After a week, remove the report and incorporate any new information to present to leadership.

- *Report in a timely way:* One goal of a mock tracer is survey preparedness via standards compliance, so addressing problems before a survey is vital. All reports should therefore be made within one month after completion of a mock tracer to allow plenty of time to correct compliance problems.

- *Accentuate the positive:* Remember to pass on positive feedback that comes to light during the mock tracer and data analysis. To encourage continued success as well as future positive interactions with the mock tracer process, reward or acknowledge departments and individuals that participate or are especially cooperative and responsive.

Applying the Results of the Mock Tracer

Step 10: Develop and Implement Improvement Plans

Your reports should indicate which problems must be addressed immediately and which can wait, which require minimal effort to correct and which require extensive effort. Employ one or more of the following improvement plan approaches to help address corrective actions:

- *Hand off to managers:* Hand off any easily addressed corrective actions that are particular to one department/ program/service to the relevant managers. Inform them of your estimates of time and resources necessary to address the problem. Offer to work with them on more complex corrective actions. Offer to repeat mock tracers to confirm findings.

- *Work with PI:* Most of what will need to be done will require integration into your organization's PI program. Follow the required approach in addressing corrective actions.

- *Check your compliance measures:* Be sure to check which elements of performance (EPs) for a Joint Commission standard require a Measure of Success (MOS). These are marked with an ⓜ. At least one measure demonstrating the effectiveness of recommended changes should be included in the action plans addressing compliance for those EPs with an ⓜ, and it must be included if the findings will be integrated into a PPR. **JCI** There is no MOS for JCI standards. Standards are Fully Met, Partially Met, Not Met,

or Not Applicable. JCI requests that a Strategic Improvement Plan (SIP) be developed by the organization for any Not Met standard(s)/measurable element(s) and/or International Patient Safety Goal(s) cited in the survey report when the organization meets the conditions for accreditation. International organizations do not complete PPRs. (*See* the discussion of PPRs in "Relate It to the Date of the Last Survey," under "Step 1: Establish a Schedule for the Mock Tracer," on page 8.)

- *Share the plans:* Make sure the entire organization is aware of the corrective actions proposed as a result of the mock tracer. Cooperation and support during future mock tracers depend on awareness of their value and follow-through. Activities and results can be shared in internal newsletters or staff meetings.

- *Monitor the plans:* The mock tracer team is not responsible for completing all the corrective actions, but it is responsible for working toward that goal by monitoring any plans based on findings from the mock tracer. Give deadlines to heads of departments/programs/services and others involved in corrective actions (in accordance with any PI policies). Check regularly on progress and make reports to leadership and the PI program on progress and cooperation.

- *Prepare for the next round:* After a few mock tracers, most organizations discover the exponential value of such exercises. They then develop a mock tracer program that allows for periodic mock tracers, sometimes with several running at one time.

OVERVIEW

Medication Management Tracers

As noted in the Introduction, tracers allow surveyors to assess organization systems and processes that drive care in the organization and affect the actual experiences of the individuals observed during the on-site evaluation.

Surveyors use the majority of their time on site performing tracers. During the tracers, surveyors assess how staff members from various disciplines work together to provide safe, high-quality care. Surveyors also talk with care recipients, when possible, to gain additional insight into their care experiences. These discussions with staff and individuals, combined with surveyors' review of documents and observations, make for a dynamic, interactive survey process.

Surveyors currently conduct individual tracers, system tracers, program-specific tracers, and environment of care (EC) tracers (which also include emergency management and life safety topics). Medication management tracers are system tracers.

Tracers are not mutually exclusive. Information gathered during one type of tracer could play a part in issues explored during subsequent tracers. For example, surveyors could choose a system tracer or initiate an EC tracer based on observations or information gleaned during an individual tracer.

System Tracers

As noted previously, medication management tracers are system tracers. A system tracer utilizes the findings from at least one individual tracer as part of an evaluation of systems/process across an organization. Medication management issues and topics are

evaluated as part of both the system tracer and the individual tracer. System tracer activity focuses on high-risk processes across organizations. The concept behind the system tracer methodology is to review processes at the organization. By examining a set of components that work together toward a common goal, the surveyor can evaluate how and how well the organization's systems function.

System tracers provide a forum for discussing important topics related to the safety and quality of care, treatment, or services *at the organization level.* Surveyors use system tracers to examine organization findings and structure and to facilitate the exchange of educational information. Although some system tracer activities might consist of a more structured discussion between staff and surveyors, the processes depend on the size of the organization and the type of system tracer.

System Tracer Topics
A system tracer generally includes an interactive discussion between a surveyor and relevant staff members. Points of discussion can include the following:
- *Process flow:* The flow of the process through the organization, including identification and management of risk points, integration of key activities, and communication among staff and units involved in the process

- *Strengths and weaknesses:* Strengths in the process and possible actions to be taken in areas that need improvement

- *Issues to explore:* Issues requiring further exploration in other survey activities

- *Compliance:* A baseline assessment of standards compliance

- *Professional development:* Education by the surveyor, as appropriate

Based on the length of the survey, which itself is based on the size, scope, and complexity of the organization, there might be one system tracer that addresses data use, medication management, and infection control. Or separate sessions could be devoted to each one of these systems. If an organization is complex and includes multiple settings and locations, three system tracers might be conducted,* and all components of the organization should be represented in the sessions. Or if medication management tracers are scheduled, they might be preceded or followed by an individual tracer focused on this topic. It could include visits to different locations in the organization. Because all survey activities are interdependent, surveyors observe and gather information about these three systems throughout the survey, not just during the sessions in which they are mentioned by name. Organizations should expect to see data use, medication management, and infection control issues brought up during individual tracers.

Medication Management System Tracers

The objective of the medication management system tracer is to evaluate the effectiveness, safety, and reliability of medication management processes and complete a high-level analysis of the medication management system. In addition, this system tracer is designed to identify potential medication management vulnerabilities, assess compliance with standards and patient safety goals, and provide education for staff and the organization as a whole on this critical component of safe, high-quality care.

This tracer is conducted in organizations with surveys lasting at least three days. The process includes a discussion and a review of medication management processes such as risk points, immediate or proximal causes for any issues, systems issues, and potential solutions, followed or preceded by an individual-based medication management system tracer. Surveyors track medication processes and handoff points, asking staff to answer questions such as, "Where does the medication 'go'?" "Why do we do what we do?" and "What systems touch a care recipient?"

Medication Management Tracer Topics

To get a better understanding of an organization's medication management system, surveyors might discuss the following topics:

- *Processes:* Medication processes, if any, that are in the scope of care, treatment, and services provided by the organization. These include the following:

◦ Selection	◦ Transcribing
◦ Procurement	◦ Preparing
◦ Storage	◦ Dispensing
◦ Securing	◦ Administration
◦ Prescribing or Ordering	◦ Monitoring

- *Patient Safety Goals:* National and International Patient Safety Goals and the organization's medication use system

- *Errors:* Reporting of errors, system breakdowns, and near misses

- *Education:* Medication education for patients and staff

- *Information management:* Information management related to medication management

- *Evaluation:* Data collection and analysis, evaluation of systems, and actions taken, including any performance improvement initiatives related to medication management

- *Risks:* Review of risk points, symptoms, and related issues

- *Medication reconciliation:* Identification of the name, dosage, route, and frequency for current medications and ordering of medications based on that

- *Patient involvement:* Care recipient involvement as part of a medication management team

Note: *Only organizations with surveys of three days' length or longer will have medication management system tracers. For organizations with surveys of shorter duration, the surveyor will focus on an important portion of the medication management issues while following an individual's receipt of care, treatment, and services in the organization. These issues will also be addressed as part of the data management system tracer. For larger organizations, these tracers include a group discussion about process issues related to medication management. Regardless of size and scope of any on-site survey, medication management issues may arise during an individual tracer, depending on where the tracer leads.*

---

* Depending on the scope and type of care, treatment, and services offered by the organization, the surveyor(s) may conduct one data use tracer. Organizations should consult their Joint Commission account representative and latest Survey Activity Guide edition for more details on the specific scope of tracers conducted during their on-site survey.

Tracer Scenarios for
HOSPITAL AND
CRITICAL ACCESS HOSPITAL

NOTE: No Two Tracers Are the Same

Please keep in mind that each tracer is unique. There is no way to know all of the questions that might be asked or documents that might be reviewed during a tracer—or what all the responses to the questions and documents might be. The possibilities are limitless, depending on the tracer topic and the organization's circumstances. These tracer scenarios and sample questions are provided as educational or training tools for organization staff; they are not scripts for real or mock tracers.

Section Elements

This section includes sample tracers—called scenarios—relevant to hospitals and critical access hospitals. The section is organized as follows:

Scenarios: Each scenario presents what might happen when a surveyor conducts a specific type of tracer. The scenarios are presented in an engaging narrative format in which the reader "follows" the surveyor through the tracer scenario. Within the narrative are bracketed numbers that correspond to numbered sample tracer questions following the tracer.

Sample Tracer Questions: After each scenario narrative is a list of sample questions a surveyor might ask during that scenario. These questions can be used to develop and conduct mock tracers in your organization on topics similar to those covered in the scenario.

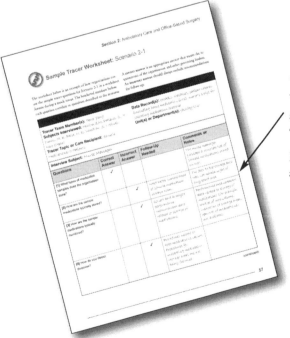

Sample Tracer Worksheet: At the end of the section is a sample worksheet that shows how the sample tracer questions for one select scenario in the section might be used in a worksheet format. The example shows how the worksheet might be completed as part of a tracer for that scenario. A blank form of the worksheet is available in Appendix B.

SCENARIO 1-1. Large Urban Hospital

Summary

In the following scenario, a surveyor conducted a medication management tracer at a large urban hospital. Within the tracer, the surveyor explored issues relating to these priority focus areas:

- Medication Management
- Assessment and Care/Services
- Physical Environment

Scenario

This medication management system tracer was scheduled for the fourth day of a five-day survey. It began with a meeting of key staff involved in the medication management system in the hospital. The objectives of the tracer were to learn about the organization's medication management processes; to evaluate those processes from planning and procurement of medications through monitoring, if applicable; and, in cases that involved prescribed medications, to evaluate the safety of using medications (*see* Appendix E, page 152) as required under National Patient Safety Goal 3.

(Bracketed numbers correlate to Sample Tracer Questions on pages 20–21.)

➜ *Meeting with Leaders.* After the surveyor was introduced to members of staff—a multidisciplinary team of key pharmacists, physicians, and nurses charged with oversight of the hospital's medication system—the group discussed the hospital's medication safety practices, how process improvements were incorporated, and how new processes were monitored. [1] The surveyor subsequently learned about the organization's medication management processes for planning, selection and procurement, storage, ordering, preparing and dispensing, administration, monitoring, and evaluation. He also learned how the organization defined and gathered information regarding medication errors and how the information was used to improve patient safety. [2–3] The surveyor then focused on risk points in the system. [4] The organization's leaders indicated that their use of chemotherapy had been identified as a high-risk activity [5], prompting the surveyor to choose this for the medication management tracer.

➜ *Meeting with the Nursing Unit Staff.* To validate the information about the medication management process as well as risk points obtained in the meeting with organization leaders, the surveyor used a previously selected patient record from

a care unit. The patient had been admitted and hospitalized three days earlier, and the surveyor had reviewed the patient's chemotherapy medication orders with staff. A nurse showed him where orders were documented on the medication administration record (MAR) and where evidence was that medications were administered in a timely manner. He also asked nurses about patient identification, processes for calculating medication doses, and validation of medication orders. [6–8] The nurses told the surveyor that in light of National Patient Safety Goal 1 (*see* Appendix E, page 151), the hospital requires the use of two patient identifiers before medication is administered. They also explained that all medication orders are weight based and calculated in collaboration with the physician.

The surveyor asked a particular nurse to explain how she administered chemotherapy medication [9–10] and about monitoring of the selected patient. The discussion revealed that there was not a standard process regarding nurses, use of personal protective equipment (PPE) to minimize exposure for chemotherapy. Additional interviews confirmed that nurses on the inpatient chemotherapy unit did not follow double-glove techniques during chemotherapy administration, as required by hospital policy. [11–12]

➜ *Questions for the Medication Room Nurse.* The surveyor moved to the medication room to observe how medications were stored. He observed that there were IVs there that should have been administered, prompting him to ask about how returns were made to the pharmacy. [13] The nurse told him that the medication was still on the unit because the IV orders had been discontinued.

The surveyor also inquired about the hospital's process of disposing of chemotherapy agents. [14] The nurse told the surveyor that opened and residual chemotherapy drugs were placed in special containers suitable for this type of drug marked "Hazardous Waste (Chemo)" and that the hospital's policy required that the containers remain closed except for times when waste was being added. The surveyor asked the nurse to describe her training in chemotherapy waste disposal. [15] She explained that she had received training in proper disposal and showed the surveyor an instructional poster at a collection point at the nursing station. The surveyor noticed a reference to a chemotherapy spill kit on the poster, prompting him to ask where the nearest kit was and what the procedures were regarding its use. [16] The nurse showed the surveyor one of several spill kits stored in the room and explained that in the event of an accident with this medication, a supervisor is immediately called. She explained that cleaning up the spill would require use of the kit's gown, gloves, spill pillows, storage bags, and other items and detailed the use of each.

➡ *Meeting with the Pharmacist.* The pharmacy had a separate IV admixture clean room that was used only for the preparation of chemotherapy medications. The pharmacist explained his role in the safe storage and preparation of these medications and also how the accuracy and appropriateness of prescriptions were assured. [17] The surveyor asked the pharmacist to explain the quality control processes required for the clean room. The pharmacist provided details regarding the orderly approach to working in the room, its negative pressure, and the procedures regarding use of its vertical flow biological safety cabinet. He pointed out that the cabinet is vented to the outside and that work on only one drug per patient was allowed in the cabinet at a time. [18]

The surveyor then discussed with the pharmacist the process from receipt of a prescription or medication order through preperation in the pharmacy. [19] The pharmacist showed the surveyor the information provided with the order to facilitate complete review of the order and proper administration of the medication. However, the pharmacist did not have details of the chemotherapy protocol used to create the order or a reference from which the order was created. The protocol was available in the patient medical record but not provided as part of the order. When comparing a chemotherapy order with the protocol, the surveyor found one instance of deviation from the protocol compared to what was ordered. [20] The pharmacist was not able to explain this. The surveyor noted that in some instances, more information should have been provided at the time of ordering of chemotherapy to facilitate proper administration, such as details related to timing for chemotherapy premedications. The surveyor also noted that when dosing reductions occur, there was little information from the prescriber regarding why. This prompted the surveyor to ask about the pharmacist's training and competencies. [21]

➡ *Moving Forward.* Based on the tracer, the surveyor may discuss the following in the Daily Briefing: providing to pharmacy details of the chemotherapy protocol available in the patient medical record to allow for a more thorough review of the order by the pharmacy, ultimately leading to proper administration of the medication; the need for a standard process and education for nurses' use of PPE to minimize exposure to chemotherapy; education for pharmacy staff about cleaning procedures between medication preparations, along with policies for monitoring compliance with cleaning procedures.

Scenario 1-1.
Sample Tracer Questions

The bracketed numbers before each question correlate to questions, observations, and data review described in the sample tracer for Scenario 1-1. You can use the tracer worksheet form in Appendix B to develop a mock tracer (*see* an example of a completed tracer worksheet at the end of this section). The information gained by conducting a mock tracer can help to highlight a good practice and/or determine issues that may require further follow-up.

Leaders:

[1] How is medication safety discussed in the organization? How are process improvements made as a result of these discussions? How do you monitor performance of new processes?

[2] How have medication errors been defined in this hospital?

[3] What information has been gathered with regard to medication errors in the hospital? How do you use this information to improve patient safety? Provide some examples.

[4] Where are the risk points in your medication management process or system? What processes were used to determine these risk points?

[5] How does the hospital evaluate medication risks and high-alert medications in particular?

Nursing Unit Staff:

[6] How do you ensure that you are administering a medication to the correct patient?

[7] Do you use the same standardized approach (pounds or kilograms) for all patients in determining the weight scheduling of their medication? How often is each patient's weight record updated?

[8] How do you work with the pharmacy and the physician when questions or concerns arise?

[9] How do you ensure that you are administering the infusion at the correct rate?

[10] What are the elements of your checking process when it comes to correct admixtures?

[11] What is organization policy regarding the use of PPE during chemotherapy administration?

[12] How are nurses who work in this area trained and deemed competent for the administration of chemotherapy medications? Of what does training

consist? How is competency assessed? Please show documentation of this assessment.

Medication Room Nurse:

[13] What is the policy regarding returns of medication to the pharmacy?

[14] How do you dispose of chemotherapy waste?

[15] How are nurses who work in this area trained and deemed competent for the administration of chemotherapy medications? Of what does training consist? How is competency assessed? Please show documentation of this assessment.

[16] Where are the nearest spill kits located? What does a kit contain? What are the procedures regarding use of the kit?

Pharmacist:

[17] What part do you play in making sure chemotherapy is used safely in this organization?

[18] Where are chemotherapy medications stored and prepared? How do you address safety issues associated with storage and preparation of chemotherapy medications?

[19] What steps do you take to ensure that preparation of chemotherapy drugs is done as safely as possible?

[20] Who oversees the process to ensure that there is consistency in meeting safe practice requirements?

[21] What are your training and competencies for the job that you do?

SCENARIO 1-2. Critical Access Hospital

Summary

In the following scenario, a surveyor conducted a medication management tracer at a critical access hospital. Within the tracer, the surveyor explored issues relating to these priority focus areas:

- Medication Management
- Assessment and Care/Services
- Communication
- Equipment Use

Scenario

The surveyor conducted a medication management system tracer at a 20-bed hospital in a rural setting. She began the

process by talking with members of the pharmacy and therapeutics committee. Participants included the risk manager, the pharmacy director, the chief nursing officer, a pharmacist, and a physician. The surveyor learned about the hospital's medication management process, including the planning, selection and procurement; storage; ordering, preparing and dispensing; administration; and monitoring of medications; and the evaluation of the medication management process. She asked the participants to provide committee meeting minutes and to discuss the organization's approach to high-alert medications.

(Bracketed numbers correlate to Sample Tracer Questions on pages 22–23.)

➡ *With the Pharmacy and Therapeutics Committee.* After learning about the organization's approach to high-alert medications during document review, [1] the surveyor was told by the committee's physician member about the organization's development and implementation of a standardized protocol for sliding-scale insulin. Committee members explained the formulary process for insulin and its storage processes, as well as how the hospital worked to prevent mix-ups. [2–3] The surveyor finished the interview with the committee by exploring medication-error reporting and new technology. Committee members reported that the organization's use of smart pumps was a crucial tool for improving the safety of IV medications. [4]

➡ *On the Nursing Unit.* The surveyor went to the nursing unit in the intensive care unit (ICU) to trace a patient with diabetic ketoacidosis. She examined processes related to insulin infusion, use of the sliding-scale insulin protocol, and daily injections.

The patient selected entered the emergency department (ED) with diabetic ketoacidosis and was then transferred to the ICU for insulin infusion. He was now on sliding-scale insulin protocol in anticipation of being converted to longer-acting insulin for use at home. The surveyor examined the medication administration record (MAR) with the nurse, asking her about insulin use for the patient. The nurse explained the use of the sliding-scale protocol for her patient and showed the surveyor where she obtained insulin from a refrigerator within an automated dispensing device. [5] When the nurse opened the refrigerator to demonstrate the process, the surveyor noticed an assortment of short-term and long-acting insulin stored together. The nurse told the surveyor that the medications all looked alike and that it was "hard to keep them straight." [6–7]

The surveyor then went with the nurse to a patient receiving an insulin infusion. The nurse told the surveyor that she had mixed the first infusion bag herself because the pharmacy department was closed and the patient was in critical condition. [8] Next, the nurse showed the surveyor the preprinted order form for the sliding-scale insulin. The surveyor asked the nurse how she administered insulin. [9] The nurse detailed the process and said that hospital policy required another nurse to check the insulin before administration. Together with a second nurse, she demonstrated the process for the surveyor, who noticed that the second nurse did not confirm that the dose drawn up was correct for the blood glucose reading in the sliding-scale protocol. The surveyor finished the tracer with the nurse by discussing the process for educating the patient about twice-a-day insulin injections that the patient would self-administer at home. [10]

→ *Interviewing the Patient.* The surveyor briefly spoke with the patient about what training he had received about his condition and about the insulin injections he would self-administer. [11–12] The patient told the surveyor that he was anticipating a visit from the dietitian and that he had talked with his care team about monitoring his blood glucose levels. He showed the surveyor a diabetes "survival skills" brochure that included personalized information, as well as a DVD that he had been given about self-injections. [13]

→ *With the Pharmacy Director.* The surveyor returned to talk with the hospital's pharmacy director about the lack of organized insulin storage he observed in the ICU. [14] The director admitted that the insulin storage the surveyor saw in the refrigerator was not in compliance with organization policy and that this was an issue that had been identified for improvement. [15] The surveyor also reviewed and discussed orders for insulin infusion with the pharmacy director and discussed the sliding-scale insulin order form and the process for reviewing orders. [16–17] Finally, she and the director explored how medication needs were met when the pharmacy was closed. [18]

→ *Moving Forward.* Based on the tracer, the surveyor may discuss the following in the Daily Briefing: ways to reduce the potential for medication mix-ups by enhancing the organization's medication storage procedures and ensuring that policies are consistently implemented successfully; encouraging nursing and pharmacy leaders to work together to get input from frontline staff about how they actually carry out their duties and about their reasons for bypassing policies—and using that feedback to identify specific causes for failures and then to test solutions; monitoring compliance and providing just-in-time training and coaching.

Scenario 1-2.
Sample Tracer Questions

The bracketed numbers before each question correlate to questions, observations, and data review described in the sample tracer for Scenario 1-2. You can use the tracer worksheet form in Appendix B to develop a mock tracer (*see* an example of a completed tracer worksheet at the end of this section). The information gained by conducting a mock tracer can help to highlight a good practice and/or determine issues that may require further follow-up.

Pharmacy and Therapeutics Committee:

[1] What high-alert medications and processes have been identified?

[2] How do you ensure that staff members are made aware of requirements for safe practices?

[3] What improvements have been made to the medication management system for high-alert medications? How are these improvements sustained? How do you know?

[4] How is compliance with proper use of technology tracked and measured? Have barriers to compliance been identified? How have barriers to compliance been addressed?

Nursing Staff:

[5] How is insulin stored?

[6] What processes are in place to minimize mix-ups of different types of insulin?

[7] Are any special precautions required for insulin storage?

[8] Are there standard concentrations for insulin admixtures? Did you mix the insulin infusion?

[9] What is the process for administering insulin? Please describe the process.

[10] Explain how you educate patients about their medications. Where is this activity documented?

Patient:

[11] Please tell me about your condition. What information have you received about your condition and the treatment you have been receiving?

[12] Do you know the warning signs of hyperglycemia and hypoglycemia?

[13] How will you manage your diabetes when you return home? Do you feel prepared to do this?

Pharmacy Director:

[14] What is the organization's policy regarding proper storage of insulin?

[15] What high-risk processes related to insulin have been identified?

[16] How was the pharmacy involved in the development of the sliding-scale protocol for insulin?

[17] How do you review the appropriateness of sliding-scale orders?

[18] What is the process for obtaining medications when the pharmacy is closed?

SCENARIO 1-3. Midsize Community Hospital

Summary

In the following scenario, a surveyor conducted a medication management tracer at a midsize community hospital. Within the tracer, the surveyor explored issues relating to these priority focus areas:

- Medication Management
- Assessment and Care/Services
- Quality Improvement Expertise/Activities
- Patient Safety

Scenario

During the medication management tracer at this 70-bed hospital, the surveyor focused on NPSG.03.05.01, which is intended to reduce the likelihood of patient harm associated with the use of anticoagulation therapy (*see* Appendix E, page 152). The surveyor met with the performance improvement (PI) director, a nurse, the hospital's pharmacist, and an elderly patient about to be discharged.

(Bracketed numbers correlate to Sample Tracer Questions on page 24.)

➡ *Meeting with the PI Director.* The PI director discussed the hospital's standardized process for dosing and monitoring of patients receiving anticoagulation therapy. The session led off with a review of the hospital's policies and procedures for heparin and warfarin therapy, in particular, and covered how compliance with the policies was evaluated. **[1–3]** She stated that the hospital complied with National Patient Safety Goal requirements regarding anticoagulant therapy. She indicated that only unit-dose oral anticoagulant products were

used as part of the hospital's efforts to reduce compounding and labeling errors. In addition, programmable smart infusion pumps were used for intravenous anticoagulant therapy. Standardized premixed infusion bags were used for heparin. **[4]**

➡ *Talking with the Nurse.* The surveyor was then introduced to a nurse, who produced an order for heparin for a surgical patient who had developed deep vein thrombosis (DVT). She told the surveyor that hospital policy required an activated partial thromboplastin time (aPPT) value every day and showed the surveyor the information in the patient's record. The nurse explained that the premixed infusion bags come from the pharmacy and showed the surveyor the infusion pump, noting that there was a minimum and maximum dose alert, which is explained to patients. **[5–9]** The nurse also said that hospital policy required double-checks and signatures when heparin therapy was initiated or when doses were altered. **[10]**

➡ *At the Patient's Bedside.* Following this session, the surveyor randomly selected a patient to discuss the care she received and the medication she been prescribed. The person chosen was a 78-year-old female patient who had undergone total hip replacement. She was alert and was able to explain her care to the surveyor. She was expecting to be discharged the next morning and had been informed that she would be prescribed warfarin. **[11–12]**

"What information have you been given about the medications you'll take after you've returned home? Has anyone talked with you about how to take warfarin safely?" the surveyor asked. **[13]** "Yes, I'm supposed to take my dose at the same time every day," the patient said, adding that she was supposed to call her doctor if she missed a dose.

"Has someone on staff here talked with you about taking other medications while you're taking warfarin and the potential for interactions?" the surveyor asked. **[14]** The patient said that she knew that aspirin and naproxen could interact with warfarin and said she had been given a brochure with information about other medications that might pose problems. The patient also said that she knew she should not drink cranberry juice while taking warfarin or make major changes to her diet. She said that a dietitian had spoken to her and provided written information about her diet. **[15]**

Completing the interview with the patient, the surveyor asked about warning signs of bleeding. The patient said that the nurse warned her that nose bleeds, black or red stools, and bleeding gums were signs that something was wrong and that she should immediately contact her doctor if any of these events occurred. [16]

➡ *With the Hospital Pharmacist.* The final stop the surveyor made during this tracer was at the hospital's pharmacy. The surveyor initiated a discussion with the pharmacist about the pharmacy's management of anticoagulation therapy, particularly ensuring accuracy of orders. [17–18] The pharmacist explained the weight-based process for dosing heparin and the standard protocol used for warfarin dosing. [19] He added that an overview of the protocol is presented at orientation for all new nurses and pharmacists and that compliance is tracked on a quarterly basis. [20] If protocol is not followed, the pharmacist is required by policy to contact the prescriber and bring the issue to the attention of the pharmacy and therapeutics committee. [21] The pharmacy had also created alerts for the clinical dietitian for potential intervention and patient education.

➡ *Moving Forward.* Based on the tracer, the surveyor may discuss the following in the Daily Briefing: the possibility of the organization adding to its anticoagulation management program other anticoagulants in addition to warfarin and heparin; adding anticoagulation therapy as a standing discussion item at weekly medication safety committee meetings so that pharmacy and nursing managers could regularly discuss any issues.

Scenario 1-3.
Sample Tracer Questions

The bracketed numbers before each question correlate to questions, observations, and data review described in the sample tracer for Scenario 1-3. You can use the tracer worksheet form in Appendix B to develop a mock tracer (*see* an example of a completed tracer worksheet at the end of this section). The information gained by conducting a mock tracer can help to highlight a good practice and/or determine issues that may require further follow-up.

PI Director:

[1] What are the hospital's policies and procedures for heparin and warfarin therapy?

[2] How were these policies developed? Who was involved?

[3] How is compliance with these policies evaluated? What improvements have been made as a result of evaluation?

[4] What steps has your organization taken to reduce anticoagulant compounding and labeling errors?

Nurse:

[5] Who is involved in the management of heparin therapy? Who manages warfarin therapy?

[6] How is the order reviewed for accuracy?

[7] How are doses adjusted? Who adjusts doses? Are they adjusted according to protocol?

[8] How is medication dispensed? What comes from the pharmacy? Is heparin provided in manufacturer-prepared premixed infusions? Is warfarin provided in unit-dose tablets in exact doses?

[9] How do you monitor and educate patients on anticoagulation therapy?

[10] Are there special requirements for infusing heparin? Explain the steps in the administration process.

Patient:

[11] What are you being treated for?

[12] Do you know what types of medications you are on now and what you will receive for use at home after discharge?

[13] Has someone on staff talked with you about the proper way to take warfarin?

[14] Has someone on staff talked with you about taking other medications while you are taking warfarin and the potential for interactions?

[15] What information have you received about your diet and its effect on the medication that you will be taking after discharge?

[16] Have you been trained in recognizing the symptoms and implications of bleeding? What should you do if bleeding or clotting occurs?

Hospital Pharmacist:

[17] How are orders reviewed for accuracy?

[18] How are orders reviewed for appropriateness? What are the elements of the review?

[19] How are doses adjusted? Who adjusts doses? Are they adjusted according to protocol?

[20] How are new members of staff made aware of the standard protocol for warfarin dosing? How is compliance monitored?

[21] Who has oversight in making sure policies and procedures regarding the management of anticoagulants are followed?

SCENARIO 1-4. Rural Hospital

Summary

In the following scenario, a surveyor conducted a medication management tracer at a rural hospital. Within the tracer, the surveyor explored issues relating to these priority focus areas:

- Medication Management
- Equipment
- Assessment and Care/Services
- Orientation and Training
- Infection Control

Scenario

During the unannounced triennial survey at a 60-bed, rural hospital, the surveyor conducted a medication management tracer on the second day of the survey. The group included the pharmacy director, performance improvement representatives, and members of nursing and medical staff leadership. The surveyor asked if any changes had occurred recently in the medication management process. Roundtable attendees told her that smart pumps were introduced to standardize concentrations of drugs. The surveyor decided to focus on smart pumps for the medication management tracer.

(Bracketed numbers correlate to Sample Tracer Questions on page 26.)

➡ *With the ICU Nurse.* The surveyor went to the intensive care unit (ICU), where she identified a patient on multiple antibiotics, dopamine, and phenylephrine infused via smart pumps. The attending physician and a nurse were both present, looking in on the patient. The surveyor asked these caregivers how they complied with the hospital's policy for identifying patients, a policy that was in line with National Patient Safety Goal 1 (*see* Appendix E, page 151). The nurse showed the surveyor how she compared the two identifiers (patient name and patient's assigned identification number) on the patient's wristband to the information on the medication administration record (MAR). [1]

Just before the physician left the area, she talked about the ordering process with the surveyor and mentioned the importance of adjusting doses according to the responses of critically ill patients. [2–5] The nurse continued the discussion with the surveyor, telling the surveyor that she was able to titrate orders. Requirements, as defined in the policy, for titrating orders included an end point by objective parameter and maximum dose allowed. [6] The surveyor looked at a dose to determine whether the parameters were met and talked with the nurse about concentrations and to the physician about dosing adjustments. The nurse then showed the surveyor how she obtained vials to prepare the first dose from an automated dispensing cabinet and explained that she would contact the pharmacy when another infusion was necessary. If her patient were critical, the nurse said that she would override the cabinet and obtain a vial to prepare the admixture. [7–9]

The surveyor concluded the ICU portion of the tracer by asking the nurse how she monitored patients and used central lines. The nurse said she had received training about central line–associated bloodstream infections and the importance of preventing these infections. [10] She also said had participated in refreshers on the topic annually since she was hired two years previously. [11]

➡ *With the Medication Room Nurse.* The surveyor next visited the medication room, where she asked a second nurse to show her how she would make the IV admixture if an emergent first dose were required. As she complied, the surveyor also asked about her knowledge regarding central lines and the prevention of related infections. [12] She also asked this nurse whether she had received training in preparing IV admixtures during in-service sessions at the hospital. The nurse replied that such sessions were not necessary because she had been trained to prepare them in nursing school. [13]

➡ *Meeting with the Pharmacy Director.* The surveyor finished the tracer by talking with the pharmacy director, who discussed his role in the medication management process for the ICU patient observed earlier. [14–17] He said that he and the nurse manager provided training on the use of smart pumps and that he maintained the drug library that supports upper dose limits for a large number of IV medications administered via the pumps. [18] He also pointed out that upgrades of pumps were the responsibility of bioengineering. However, the pharmacy director said he reviewed situations where a nurse would withdraw a medication from the automated dispensing cabinet prior to his validation of the order (overrides) and thought that the nurses were typically too quick to access the cabinets. [19–21]

➡ *Moving Forward.* Based on the tracer, the surveyor may discuss the following in the Daily Briefing: education policies for nursing staff and whether such policies are being followed, especially in regard to NPSG.07.04.01 (*see* Appendix E, page 153), which in part requires that staff receive education related to preventing central line–associated bloodstream infections upon hire and annually thereafter; increasing the focus on assessing competencies, particularly in the preparation of IV admixtures; consideration of overrides of automated dispensing cabinets as an area for risk assessment and performance improvement.

Scenario 1-4.
Sample Tracer Questions

The bracketed numbers before each question correlate to questions, observations, and data review described in the sample tracer for Scenario 1-4. You can use the tracer worksheet form in Appendix B to develop a mock tracer (*see* an example of a completed tracer worksheet at the end of this section). The information gained by conducting a mock tracer can help to highlight a good practice and/or determine issues that may require further follow-up.

ICU and Physician Nurse:

[1] How do you confirm the identity of your patients for medication management?

[2] Discuss the process of ordering the medications your patients currently receive.

[3] How are these medications prescribed?

[4] Do doses need to be weight based?

[5] Provide details regarding your approach to adjusting doses according to the responses of critically ill patients.

[6] What does your policy say about titrating doses?

[7] How are titrated doses calculated? Show me how you would calculate a dose for this particular patient.

[8] What is the process for administration of a dose? Show me how you set up the smart pump. Do you take any special precautions, such as a two-nurse check?

[9] Do you ever make infusions in the ICU? What about emergent first doses? Where are these prepared? How do you know what concentrations to prepare?

[10] Have you received any education about how to prevent central line–associated bloodstream infections?

[11] How have your competencies to prepare sterile IV preparations been assessed?

Medication Room Nurse:

[12] How are staff educated about central line–

associated bloodstream infections and the importance of prevention? When does education occur?

[13] How have the appropriate competencies for the preparation of IV compounded sterile products been determined?

Pharmacy Director:

[14] What is your role in the care of patients receiving medication via smart pumps?

[15] Are custom admixtures ever prepared?

[16] Are orders reviewed for appropriateness? Is any other monitoring performed?

[17] Are any antibiotics restricted?

[18] How are you involved in the organization's use of smart pumps?

[19] Are these medications able to be obtained prior to a pharmacist review, using an override process from the automated dispensing cabinet?

[20] Are the nurses trained about the high error rates related to overrides?

[21] Does the hospital evaluate overrides for type and frequency? If so, how is this done? If not, why is this not done?

SCENARIO 1-5. Large Teaching Hospital

Summary

In the following scenario, a surveyor conducted a medication management tracer at a large teaching hospital. Within the tracer, the surveyor explored issues relating to these priority focus areas:
- Medication Management
- Assessment and Care/Services
- Quality Improvement Expertise/Activities

Scenario

The surveyor conducted several individual patient tracers in this teaching hospital with more than 600 beds before moving on to a medication management system tracer. This tracer took place during the fourth day of a five-day survey.

(Bracketed numbers correlate to Sample Tracer Questions on pages 27–28.)

➡ *Pharmacy and Therapeutics Committee Session.* The surveyor asked the members of the pharmacy and therapeutics committee to describe the medication management process in the organization as well as risk points in the system. [1] Discussion revealed a perception among the group that there had been a large number of missing medications on various nursing units. The members of the committee also said that there had been problems with physician orders for medications due to illegible handwriting. In addition, when a medication was not available on a nursing unit, a nurse called for a stat medication or took the medication from floor stock prior to verification by the pharmacist.

Committee members identified concentrated sodium chloride as a problematic medication in their organization due to its inherent risks and had implemented policies and procedures over the past year to address associated issues. [2–4] Specifically, the hospital had limited where concentrated electrolytes were allowed outside the pharmacy and had created tighter controls for who was allowed to access such medications. Requests to store concentrated electrolytes outside the pharmacy (albeit a rare occurrence) required approval from the committee. In addition, the pharmacy provided oversight to ensure that these areas really did have a critical patient need for this medication, that staff were competent to manage it, and that it was clearly labeled and accompanied with warnings about proper dilution and administration rate. [5]

➡ *Meeting with the Nursing Unit Staff.* Regarding the issue of missing medications, the surveyor first talked with nurses on the unit. He asked how often they thought medicines disappeared, to which a nurse responded, "Frequently." The surveyor then asked about the processes for identifying patients, validating medication doses, [6] and transmitting orders to the pharmacy. [7] At the surveyor's request, a nurse showed the surveyor how orders were transmitted by scanner to the pharmacy. The surveyor also asked about stat orders. [8] A nurse told him that her primary concern was getting her patients the medications they needed and getting them on time. She added that she was not worried about bypassing a review by the pharmacy because she consulted nursing guidelines for dosages. [9–10]

➡ *Talking with the Pharmacist.* The surveyor followed up on the reports of missing medications by asking the pharmacist for his thoughts about the causes of missing medications on patient care units. [11] The pharmacist showed him several blank pieces of paper and explained that every day he received blank faxes like this instead of medication orders. The

pharmacist also said that duplicate orders were sometimes sent by nurses who were not sure if the pharmacy had received a fax. [12] He also informed the surveyor that, in his opinion, a breakdown in quality control in both general procedures and in nurses' training on how to send orders was the cause of several problems. [13–14]

➡ *Moving Forward.* Based on the tracer, the surveyor may discuss the following in the Daily Briefing: improving the legibility of handwritten orders to reduce transcription errors and perhaps requiring a second member of the staff to collaborate on such orders to try to reduce risks; lack of safety checks when nurses pull stat medications from the automated dispensing machine without allowing for a pharmacy review of the order; using a recognized performance improvement methodology to examine issues related to physician orders for medications.

Scenario 1-5.
Sample Tracer Questions

The bracketed numbers before each question correlate to questions, observations, and data review described in the sample tracer for Scenario 1-5. You can use the tracer worksheet form in Appendix B to develop a mock tracer (*see* an example of a completed tracer worksheet at the end of this section). The information gained by conducting a mock tracer can help to highlight a good practice and/or determine issues that may require further follow-up.

Pharmacy and Therapeutics Committee:

[1] What risk points in the medication management system have you identified?

[2] How is the organization addressing these risk points?

[3] What improvements have you made to the medication management system as a result of regular evaluation?

[4] What types of medications are most often prescribed in the nursing units? Name about 10 of them. Which on this list are considered by the organization to be "problematic"?

[5] What policies have been implemented specifically to control unwanted issues surrounding "problematic" medications?

Nursing Unit Staff:

[6] What is your organization's process for validating medication orders?

(continued)

Scenario 1-5.
Sample Tracer Questions (continued)

[7] What is the process for transmitting orders to the pharmacy?

[8] What medication management work-arounds are you aware of in your units that could be considered security risk points?

[9] What training has been provided to the nursing staff regarding high error rates related to overrides?

[10] Has your pharmacy provided training regarding the error-reduction potential of a pharmacist review of medication orders?

Pharmacist:

[11] Are you aware of any work-arounds in the medication order submission process that could be considered security risk points?

[12] What is the correct process for receiving orders?

[13] What are your systems for quality control when medication orders are filled?

[14] How is the pharmacy involved in quality improvement activities?

SCENARIO 1-6. Children's Hospital

Summary

In the following scenario, a surveyor conducted a medication management tracer at a children's hospital. Within the tracer, the surveyor explored issues relating to these priority focus areas:

- Medication Management
- National Patient Safety Goals
- Quality Improvement Expertise/Activities

Scenario

The medication management system tracer was scheduled for the third day of a four-day survey at a 200-bed children's hospital. This system tracer began with a meeting of key staff involved in the hospital's medication management system. The meeting included general discussion and review of materials related to medication planning, selection and procurement, storage, ordering, preparing and dispensing, administration, monitoring, and evaluation. Staff said that they had chosen to focus on improving heparin safety after hearing news reports of errors involving

pediatric patients and look-alike/sound-alike mix-ups with heparin concentrations. Heparin, they knew, was a known contributor to increased risks of adverse drug events due to the complexity of its dosing and the difficulty in monitoring its effects. Thus, the surveyor decided to add a focus on use of heparin, which, as an antigoagulant, is the subject of NPSG.03.05.01 (*see* Appendix E, page 152).

(Bracketed numbers correlate to Sample Tracer Questions on page 29.)

➡ *Report from the Pharmacy and Therapeutics Staff.* Representatives from the pharmacy and therapeutics staff in attendance at the meeting shared information with the surveyor about the hospital's efforts to safely manage heparin use, explaining that the organization had moved to limit concentrations. In the past, the drug was delivered and stored in various concentrations to facilitate infusions. The hospital had also worked to limit the number of steps prior to the administration of the drug. Foremost among the hospital's efforts was the introduction of bar-code label scanning as a new smart pump feature. [1] The manufacturer's bar-code label on a premixed heparin container could be scanned, and the correct drug and concentration could be automatically selected from the pump library. However, this technology was just being phased in, so part of the process still relied on manual procedures.

➡ *With the Frontline Nurse.* From among the documents the surveyor received, the surveyor was able to target a patient receiving heparin and to review that patient's record. The surveyor found that a nurse had selected the patient's medication from the automated dispensing machine (ADM). [2] Moving to the nursing unit, the surveyor reviewed the physician's written order for the patient. It had been transmitted to the pharmacy by fax for pharmacist review and verification before the nurse could withdraw the medication from the ADM. [3–4] In a meeting with the nurse who withdrew the medication, the surveyor asked what would occur if he needed the medication before the pharmacy had a chance to verify the order. The nurse said that in this situation, he would override the ADM. [5]

The nurse explained how he identified patients, according to hospital policy, and how medication doses were validated. The surveyor was able to observe the process the nurse used to obtain heparin from the ADM. [6] Afterwards, the nurse said that all heparin concentrations were standardized and that, with a bar code, he could quickly go to a drawer to pull the necessary dosage without going through extra steps to validate the correct dosage. [7]

➡️ *Talking with the Pharmacy Staff.* The surveyor moved from the nursing unit to the pharmacy to trace that department's role in safely managing heparin. A pharmacy technician showed the surveyor how she used the bar-coding process to re-stock the ADM. **[8]** The technician referred to the previously discussed bar-coded label scanning for smart pumps. **[9]** She also pointed out that the number of premixed formulations had been dramatically reduced to only a few products. **[10]**

The surveyor finished his pharmacy review by meeting with the pharmacy director. The director shared information about the pharmacy's involvement in the hospital's anticoagulation program, which included medication reconciliation, drug interaction avoidance, clinical trial support, and patient and staff education. **[11]** In addition to implementing the bar-code program, the pharmacy director said that the pharmacy was developing a comprehensive intranet site that would provide background information, guidelines and protocols, dosing nomograms, referral forms, patient teaching tools, references, and other helpful information. **[12]**

➡️ *Moving Forward.* Based on the tracer, the surveyor may discuss the following in the Daily Briefing: enhancing the organization's use of systems (drug libraries and bar-code scanning for the ADM) rather than focusing solely on the accountability of nurses, physicians, and pharmacy staff, perhaps by examining ways for pharmacists to have a more consistent presence on care units to observe and assist with medication management issues.

Scenario 1-6.
Sample Tracer Questions

The bracketed numbers before each question correlate to questions, observations, and data review described in the sample tracer for Scenario 1-6. You can use the tracer worksheet form in Appendix B to develop a mock tracer (*see* an example of a completed tracer worksheet at the end of this section). The information gained by conducting a mock tracer can help to highlight a good practice and/or determine issues that may require further follow-up.

Pharmacy and Therapeutics Staff:

[1] How are you addressing safety risks related to heparin? What steps are you taking to manage the use of this medication safely?

Frontline Nurse:

[2] What are your organization's policy/procedures on use of an ADM?

[3] What is the approved process for transmitting orders to the pharmacy?

[4] Are there specific or unique steps to follow in withdrawing heparin or other high-alert medications from an ADM?

[5] What do you do if you do not receive a needed medication from the pharmacy?

[6] What orientation, training, and competency assessments qualify you to administer heparin?

[7] Are any additional checks needed other than the bar code? For example, do you compare the medication label to the order and verify the route of administration, times, and dosage?

Pharmacy Staff:

[8] Describe in detail the steps you take in restocking the ADM.

[9] Describe the entire process you use from receipt of heparin orders through stocking the ADM.

[10] What other safety checks are in place beyond the bar-code system?

[11] How are you involved in the hospital's safety efforts related to anticoagulation?

[12] Is the pharmacy itself involved in its own safety efforts and performance improvement projects related to anticoagulants?

SCENARIO 1-7. Community Hospital

Summary

In the following scenario, a surveyor conducted a medication management tracer at a 180-bed community hospital. Within the tracer, the surveyor explored issues relating to these priority focus areas:
- Medication Management
- Orientation & Training
- Patient Safety
- Equipment Use
- Quality Improvement Expertise/Activities

Scenario

The surveyor asked about ordering/prescribing procedures and about pharmacy protocols for dispensing medications. The surveyor asked to see reports of adverse drug events (ADEs) and near misses. For this medication management tracer she selected a near-miss report involving a 4-year-old boy. During the course of this tracer, issues raised concerning contracted services necessitated additional tracer activity. Thus, this scenario is an example of a second generation tracer, which takes an in-depth look at a high-risk topic (*see* "Introduction," page 2).

(Bracketed numbers correlate to Sample Tracer Questions on pages 31–32.)

➜ *Talking with the Pharmacist.* The surveyor first talked with the pharmacy in following up on the pediatric patient near miss. [1–2] The pharmacist explained that the patient was prescribed a wrong dose of vancomycin because of a switch in dosing weight from kilograms to pounds. The pharmacist explained that he had ultimately caught the error when he reviewed the order. [3]

The surveyor then asked the pharmacist whom he had notified about the error. [4–6] The pharmacist said he had notified the pharmacy director, but did not know if the director had informed the hospital. The pharmacist, who had begun work at the pharmacy just a few weeks earlier, explained that he worked for a national company contracted by the hospital to provide medications and pharmaceutical services. Since he had caught the mistake before the medication was given to the patient, he felt there was no harm done and that it would not matter if it took a month or so to report the error. At that moment, the surveyor realized that she would need to take an in-depth look at the hospital's contracted services as soon as she finished the medication management tracer.

The pharmacist and surveyor then discussed ways the pharmacy worked to ensure safe medication management practices. The pharmacist said that the hospital had a bar-code medication verification process, but this process would not have caught the near-miss dosing error they had been talking about. [7–8] The surveyor and pharmacist also discussed the pharmacy's role in the hospital's medication management process, including its procedures in drawing up patient-specific doses.

➜ *Questioning the Pediatric Ward Nurse.* The surveyor then proceeded to the pediatric unit to trace another patient who had also suffered an ADE involving vancomycin. In this case, she explored the medication management process regarding the care of a child with a ureteral stricture. The child had developed hypertension as a result of collateral kidney damage. A review of the medical record showed that the patient was taking antihypertensive medications, including captopril, spironolactone, and furosemide. The boy was also placed on vancomycin therapy as a result of a cellulitis culture that had revealed methicillin-resistant *Staphylococcus aureus* (MRSA).

The surveyor asked the child's nurse to explain how patients should be weighed to determine appropriate dosage. The nurse said that all patient weights must be recorded in kilograms. The surveyor then asked the nurse to show her the medications the patient had received, and together they reviewed the medication administration record (MAR) and discussed prescriptions policies and dose preparation. [9–11] The surveyor next asked to see syringes and found patient-specific doses as well as bar-code labeling that was not attached to the doses. [12] The nurse said that the children's syringes were so small that properly wrapping the bar-code label so that the scanner could read it was difficult and created problems. She said that bar codes often failed for that reason. [13–14]

➜ *Returning to the Pharmacist.* The surveyor returned to the pharmacist to follow up on the issues prompted by the MRSA diagnosis in the second pediatric patient. She asked the pharmacist if the organization had an antimicrobial stewardship program. [15] The pharmacist said that he served as a key member of the hospital's multidisciplinary antimicrobial stewardship team, which had developed practice guidelines and pathways along with education programs. Other antimicrobial stewardship team members included an infection control professional, a microbiologist, an infectious diseases physician, a representative from information management, a nursing leader, the hospital's epidemiologist, and an administrative leader. The pharmacist added that the team worked closely with the hospital's pharmacy and therapeutics committee. The surveyor asked the pharmacist what training he had received that qualified him to serve on the antimicrobial stewardship team. [16] The pharmacist described his professional credentials and said that the hospital had provided additional training when he'd joined the team.

The surveyor asked if the antimicrobial stewardship team monitored vancomycin use. [17] The pharmacist replied that the organization did track use of this antibiotic, using guidelines from the Healthcare Infection Control Practices Advisory Committee of the Centers for Disease Control and Prevention. The surveyor completed the discussion with the pharmacist by asking which health care–associated infections (HAIs) the organization tracked and how the organization used the information it obtained to determine formulary restrictions. [18]

➜ *Concluding with the Medical Director.* The surveyor concluded the medication management tracer by meeting with the hospital medical director. She asked how the hospital verified competency. [19] The medical director replied that nurses and other hospital staff undergo a competency assessment upon hire and then annually thereafter. These assessments are documented in the personnel record, the director added, and showed the surveyor the record for the pediatric ward nurse with whom she had spoken. The surveyor confirmed that the nurse's competency had been assessed, verified, and documented. The medical director explained that for pharmacists, verification of competency was the responsibility of the pharmacy, as provided for in the contractual agreement between the hospital and the pharmacy.

➡️ *Talking with the Pharmacy Director.* Turning her attention to the issue of the contracted services between the national company and the hospital, the surveyor wanted first to talk to the pharmacy director, whom she was able to reach by phone. Interested in the depth of the director's involvement with the pharmacy and the hospital, she asked about his relationship with both and how often he was actually on the premises. [20] The director explained that he traveled among a large number of hospitals and other health care organizations in the area for which his company provided services. He was at this particular hospital about once a month. He answered additional questions from the surveyor about his participation on this facility's various committees, [21] the methods and frequency of communication with the hospital, [22] and the kinds of training and orientation pharmacy staff received. [23]

➡️ *Conferring with the Chief Operating Officer.* Finally, the surveyor met with the hospital's chief operating officer, who managed the pharmacy contract. She asked to see a copy of the contract, [24] which she examined before they talked. She then asked extensive questions regarding the hospital's relationship with the company providing it pharmacy services. [25–26] The officer responded with information about the organization's need for pharmacy services and the complete history of its affiliation with the national company. Their discussion eventually turned to performance expectations and the methods and frequency of evaluations regarding this performance. [27–28] The surveyor also asked about any other contracted services agreements the hospital had and requested reviews of each contract.

➡️ *Moving Forward.* Based on the medication management tracer, the surveyor may discuss the following in the Daily Briefing: performing a root cause analysis on dosing near misses in order to understand risk points in weight-based dosing processes; conducting a failure mode and effects analysis (FMEA) or using process improvement tools to examine the potential for errors associated with pediatric syringes and bar-code labeling and scanning; staying focused on antimicrobial

stewardship as an integral component of infection control efforts.

Based on the further examination of contracted pharmacy services, the surveyor might discuss the hospital's overall contract process.

Scenario 1-7.
Sample Tracer Questions

The bracketed numbers before each question correlate to questions, observations, and data review described in the sample tracer for Scenario 1-7. You can use the tracer worksheet form in Appendix B to develop a mock tracer (*see* an example of a completed tracer worksheet at the end of this section). The information gained by conducting a mock tracer can help to highlight a good practice and/or determine issues that may require further follow-up.

Pharmacist:

[1] Is there a pediatric formulary? If so, are prescribers aware of the medications on this list?

[2] How is the review of prescriptions conducted? What policies guide practice?

[3] What is the pharmacist's role in reviewing vancomycin therapy as a retrospective process and regarding real-time monitoring of current patient therapy?

[4] What happened after this near miss was identified? Has a root cause analysis been performed?

[5] Have the prescriber and the nurse been informed of the findings following an evaluation and analysis of the near miss?

[6] What happens with medication error data? Have you seen any changes when a medication error is identified?

[7] Are bar-code bypasses tracked? Explain how.

[8] How are bypasses analyzed?

Pediatric Ward Nurse:

[9] How are medications provided for pediatric patients? Who prepares them?

[10] How are medications prescribed? What policies are in place related to prescribing?

[11] What medications are parts of floor stock? If you need to prepare a dose of medication, what is the process for doing so?

(continued)

Scenario 1-7.
Sample Tracer Questions (continued)

[12] Do you review the medication label to see if it includes the required information?

[13] How does the bar-code process work? How do you use it for stat medications or for partial doses from vials or containers that are pulled from floor stock?

[14] How are medication errors reported? What procedure does the organization follow if an error is caught before it reaches the patient? Have you ever reported an error or a near miss?

Pharmacist (Revisited):

[15] Does the organization have an antimicrobial stewardship program? If not, how do you ensure that antimicrobial agents are used properly? If so, what are the antimicrobial stewardship activities? Describe the process and its outcomes.

[16] What training have you received that qualifies you to serve on the antimicrobial stewardship team?

[17] Does the antimicrobial stewardship team track the use of vancomycin? How does it use that information?

[18] Does the organization track MRSA incidence? What other HAIs does it track? How is information about HAI rates used in the antimicrobial stewardship program?

Medical Director:

[19] How does the hospital verify competency? How often is competency assessed? How is verification of competency documented?

Pharmacy Director:

[20] What is your role as pharmacy director? What are your responsibilities? How frequently are you on-site at the hospital pharmacy?

[21] Are you part of the hospital's pharmaceutical and therapeutics committee? Are you a member of any other committees at this hospital?

[22] What reports do you routinely submit to the hospital? How frequently are these reports submitted?

[23] What orientation do your company's employees receive from the hospital?

Chief Operating Officer:

[24] Please show me a copy of the contract with the pharmacy. How is the contract managed?

[25] How would you describe your hospital's relationship with the contract company?

[26] What is the role of hospital leadership in relation to contracted services?

[27] What performance criteria for contracted staff are set in advance? How do you monitor performance? How frequently is performance evaluated? When was the last time performance was evaluated?

[28] What contractual provisions are made for medical staff oversight? When was the last review by medical staff?

SCENARIO 1-8. Inpatient Psychiatric Care Unit of a Hospital

Summary

In the following scenario, a surveyor conducted a medication management tracer in an inpatient psychiatric care unit of a hospital. Within the tracer, the surveyor explored issues relating to these priority focus areas:

- Medication Management
- Leadership and Planning
- Patient Care and Assessment
- Patient and Family Education

Scenario

A group of surveyors conducted a survey in a 300-bed general hospital that also provided behavioral health/psychiatric services. Inpatient care was provided to adults, adolescents, and children, but the services did not include a forensic care unit. The surveyor gathered information through interviews, observations, patient medical records, and other documents regarding medication management processes in the organization's behavioral health/psychiatric services areas. Although these services were part of the general hospital, the surveyor noted that discussions with pharmacy and therapeutics staff members and the minutes of the executive committee of the medical staff did not seem to reveal any mention of behavioral health.

Individual patient tracers of the hospital's behavioral health patients did not identify any particular medication challenges. Survey team members discussed the issue and agreed that pharmacists did not seem to be engaged in reviewing medication use in that service. The survey was long enough to allow for system tracers related to data use, infection control, and medication use.

(Bracketed numbers correlate to Sample Tracer Questions on page 34.)

➡ *At the Leadership Meeting.* After the document review, the surveyor decided to start the medication management tracer by talking with hospital leaders. The leaders told him that the hospital does deal with some challenging medications, but they are medications that are typically used in other hospitals throughout the country. The surveyor found that storage of and access to concentrated electrolytes, opioid medications, chemotherapy, anticoagulants, and IV preparations were appropriate and that there were no particular issues related to any of them.

The surveyor then asked the leaders how the behavioral health/psychiatric services were integrated into the overall medication management of the hospital. **[1]** The leaders indicated that pharmacists did not work with the behavioral health staff in reviewing individual medication therapy for each patient. **[2–3]** They admitted that there had been problems with medication reconciliation for the behavioral health patient population. Patients were frequently confused regarding the medications they were taking—especially geriatric and non-compliant patients, as well as patients with comorbidities, such as addictions and pain management issues. **[4]**

The leaders said that there were no issues with the availability of medications for the behavioral health patient population. Medications commonly used for such patients—anti-anxiety medications, antidepressants, antipsychotics, and so forth—were included on the formulary. The leaders at the meeting were unable to discuss any required monitoring associated with these medications. No one who was familiar with the various behavioral health units was at the meeting, and the leaders were not familiar with any recent improvements to any parts of the medication management system. **[5]**

In his quest to dig deeper, the surveyor decided to speak to members of staff on each of the organization's primary behavioral health areas.

➡ *Questions for the Pediatric Behavioral Health Unit Physician.* He began with a visit to a physician on the pediatric unit who had gathered medication history information on patients and included it as part of the admission notes. **[6–7]** However, the physician indicated that the pediatric be-

havioral health unit did not use a standardized process for medication reconciliation. The surveyor decided to focus on a patient from the unit who had been hospitalized for three days. He noted no problems with this patient's medication orders or documentation on the medication administration record (MAR). In addition, the surveyor noted that the patient's medication was administered in a timely manner. Nurses had properly identified the patient before administering medication to her, and the patient's orders, MAR, and pharmacy records seemed to match. Generally, storage and handling of medications in the unit seemed appropriate. **[8]**

➡ *Questions for the Adolescent Behavioral Health Unit Physician and Nurse.* A short time later, the physician on duty on the adolescent behavioral health unit also told the surveyor that she gathered patients' medication history information and included it as part of the admission notes. The surveyor could not tell whether staff were using any standardized process for medication reconciliation, and the physician was unable to verify it, either. **[9]** Other members of the unit's staff told the surveyor that the medication history was sometimes unreliable, particularly with regard to "other medications" and alcohol and marijuana. But all adolescents were given urine screens for substance abuse, the staff members said, and explained the process for this screening to the surveyor.

The surveyor decided to trace a patient on this unit who had been admitted through the emergency department. The patient selected had a history of depression and substance abuse. Nurses told the surveyor that this adolescent patient was noncompliant with prescribed medications before being admitted and that his drug screens indicated the presence of medications other than those he should have been taking. The patient's record showed that appropriate laboratory testing for liver function had been conducted. **[10]** It was not clear how thorough the medication reconciliation process had been at admittance. Patient and family education had not been documented, but a nurse said it had been performed. **[11]**

➡ *Questions for the Adult Behavioral Health Unit Nurses.* Nurses on the adult behavioral unit told the surveyor that the unit had a large and growing population of geriatric patients, many of whom had been referred from the general hospital. They explained that they were not aware of any formal effort by the organization to identify trends in this area. The scope of services for geriatric care was changing, they said, but leaders of the organization did not seem to recognize the impact of these types of patients on readmissions to the hospital.

The nursing staff reported that some of the patients had been on medications at home that may have led to their hospitalization. They also said that patients were both undermedicated and overmedicated prior to admission and that the geriatric service was trying to address this challenge. Finally, they said that the pharmacy department was not closely involved with the unit and that there was a lack of systematic thinking that might have improved patient compliance with discharge instructions or patient/family education. **[12–13]**

➡ *Report from the Pharmacist.* Later, in a meeting with the pharmacist, the surveyor was told that his department did check for medication incompatibilities, but admitted that it had not been engaged in ensuring systematic medication management for behavioral health patients. **[14–17]** The pharmacist expressed his belief that more active involvement in medication management for behavioral health patients would be beneficial. **[18]**

➡ *Moving Forward.* Based on the tracer, the surveyor may discuss the following in the Daily Briefing: strengthening the organization's medication reconciliation processes for all of the units providing behavioral health services (noting, for example, that medication history obtained in the general hospital for geriatric patients was present, but may have qualitative holes in it due to a lack of an effective medication reconciliation process, including patient education); increasing the organization's concentration on leadership and planning so its scope of service adequately supports the expanding patient population in its behavioral health units.

Scenario 1-8.
Sample Tracer Questions

The bracketed numbers before each question correlate to questions, observations, and data review described in the sample tracer for Scenario 1-8. You can use the tracer worksheet form in Appendix B to develop a mock tracer (*see* an example of a completed tracer worksheet at the end of this section). The information gained by conducting a mock tracer can help to highlight a good practice and/or determine issues that may require further follow-up.

Leaders:

[1] Describe the medication management system for the inpatient behavioral health units.

[2] Is there anything different about the medication management systems in these areas than in other areas of the organization?

[3] How do pharmacists and physicians interact to improve medication management processes in these units?

[4] What types of data are collected to document the problems and to guide improvements to the medication management processes in these units?

[5] Have any improvements been made to the medication management system in these units in the past year? How are these improvements sustained? How do you know?

Behavioral Health Unit Staff:

[6] What process do you use to obtain a patient's history?

[7] What is your role in the medication management system?

[8] Walk me through your processes for the storage, ordering, preparing and dispensing, and administration of medications on this unit.

[9] Explain how you reconcile medications at admission. What are the steps? How is this process documented?

[10] How do you monitor patients to determine the effects of medications?

[11] What instructions do you give patients and/or families regarding their medication? How is this process documented?

[12] Does each patient and/or family receive a complete list of medications at discharge? How is this process documented?

[13] Are you involved in any performance improvement activities related to medication management?

Pharmacist:

[14] Does a pharmacist review all prescriptions?

[15] What are your role and your department's role in collaborating with behavioral health units?

[16] What is the process for developing a completed list of medications a patient is taking at admission?

[17] What is the process for developing a list of discharge medications?

[18] What opportunities for improvement do you see in working with the behavioral health units?

SCENARIO 1-9. Family Practice Primary Care Facility

Summary

In the following scenario, a surveyor conducted a medication management system tracer in a family practice primary care facility. Within the tracer, the surveyor explored issues relating to these priority focus areas:

- Communication
- Infection Control
- Orientation & Training
- Patient Safety

Scenario

During the medication management tracer at this primary care hospital, the surveyor met with the nursing coordinator, several practice leaders, and a physician involved in oversight of medication management. This tracer took place during the third day of a five-day survey.

(Bracketed numbers correlate to Sample Tracer Questions on page 36.)

➡ *Reviewing with Leaders and Staff.* The surveyor asked for an overview of the hospital's medication management process as well as the group's opinions on identified high-risk areas. [1–2] The nursing coordinator and physician reported that poor patient compliance was the most common and most serious risk. They also agreed with the practice leaders' opinion that the physicians' habit of giving patients sample medications without written instructions from the pharmacist may be exacerbating this problem.

The surveyor asked about the group's experiences and training related to medication management oversight. [3] He learned that physicians bore most of the responsibility for clinical oversight of medication management. Practice leaders met periodically to discuss medication management issues, while the nursing coordinator described her role as administrative in nature. [4]

➡ *Reviewing with the Nursing Coordinator.* The surveyor asked the nursing coordinator how the organization determined which medications were high-alert ones and which ones were deemed look-alike/sound-alike medications. [5] The nursing coordinator said that look-alike/sound-alike medication pairs were selected some time ago and that this standard list was reviewed at least annually. Such medications, she said, were labeled and identified in the storage room. [6] The sur-

veyor then asked the coordinator what training was provided by the organization regarding look-alike/sound-alike medications, as well as for the identification of high-alert medications. [7] The coordinator explained that these medications were all supposed to be stored only in the medication room, making training on the topic unnecessary.

The surveyor told the nursing coordinator that he had observed medication storage in the emergency cart outside the medication storage room when he had conducted individual patient tracers. She pointed out that the emergency cart was only to be used in serious patient emergencies, and in these situations, staff simply had to administer what the physician ordered. [8] The surveyor observed the medication storage room in the facility. He noted that the high-alert sample medications were clearly identified with colored labels. There was also fluorescent green labeling on the shelves and boxes for look-alike/sound-alike medications, but the nursing coordinator said this special labeling was done only in the medication storage room, and only nursing and medical staff had access to this room. When the surveyor checked the storage boxes, he noticed that some of them actually contained other medications that were not identified on the outside of the boxes. [9] The nursing coordinator said that she wanted to get another storage system but had been told that the budget did not allow for that.

➡ *With the Vaccination Administration Area Nurse.* Next, the surveyor observed the vaccination administration area. He found boxes of vaccines stored in a refrigerator—a unit equipped with a thermometer—as well as bottles of drinking water. The nurse in charge of vaccinations said that she knew that organization policy required food items to be stored separately from medication storage areas, but she felt that water was not food. [10] Additionally, she noted that the unit had only the single refrigerator. The surveyor also observed that boxes of injection needles were stored directly on the floor. [11] The nurse said that she knew this was not acceptable and that the hospital needed more space and more shelves.

➡ *Moving Forward.* Based on the tracer, the surveyor may discuss the following in the Daily Briefing: the need for greater systems thinking (pointing out that inconsistent storage practices in the organization posed serious risks for medication errors, as did the lack of education regarding high-alert medications).

Scenario 1-9.
Sample Tracer Questions

The bracketed numbers before each question correlate to questions, observations, and data review described in the sample tracer for Scenario 1-9. You can use the tracer worksheet form in Appendix B to develop a mock tracer (*see* an example of a completed tracer worksheet at the end of this section). The information gained by conducting a mock tracer can help to highlight a good practice and/or determine issues that may require further follow-up.

Leaders and Staff:

[1] What is your medication management process? Who has responsibility for medication management?

[2] What are the high-risk areas you have identified in your medication management process? How have you identified these areas?

[3] What kind of background and training have you received to assist you in performing duties related to medication management oversight? Do you receive any ongoing training and access to resources?

[4] How often does the organization arrange time to discuss medication management issues?

Nursing Coordinator:

[5] What high-alert medications and look-alike/sound-alike medications do you keep in the hospital?

[6] Where are these high-alert medications stored? How are they labeled? What special processes are used for storage and labeling of look-alike/sound-alike medications?

[7] What training and information do you share with staff about these types of medications?

[8] Show me where you store medications. What is your process for their safe storage?

[9] How do you ensure that medications are not placed in the wrong locations? How do you monitor for this?

Vaccination Administration Area Nurse:

[10] What is the policy on safely storing vaccines? What else is allowed to be in the refrigerators where you keep these vaccines?

[11] What do you do when you do not have enough space to store all your supplies? In such a situation, what do you do with high-risk items such as injection needles?

Sample Tracer Worksheet: Scenario 1-1.

The worksheet below is an example of how organizations can use the sample tracer questions for Scenario 1-1 in a worksheet format during a mock tracer. The bracketed numbers before each question correlate to questions described in the scenario.

A **correct answer** is an appropriate answer that meets the requirements of the organization and other governing bodies. An **incorrect answer** should always include recommendations for follow-up.

Tracer Team Member(s): Jade Caldwell
Subjects Interviewed: Darryl Magnus, Karin Lacek, Dorie Prine, Anita Kaye, Ed Montenegro
Tracer Topic or Care Recipient: Chemotherapy, chemotherapy patient

Data Record(s): Chemotherapy patient record, MAR, instructional poster on hazardous waste disposal, chemotherapy order, chemotherapy protocol
Unit(s) or Department(s): Oncology unit, hospital pharmacy

Interview Subject: Leaders

Questions	Correct Answer	Incorrect Answer	Follow-Up Needed	Comments or Notes
[1] How is medication safety discussed in the organization? How are process improvements made as a result of these discussions? How do you monitor performance of new processes?	✓			
[2–3] How have medication errors been defined in this hospital? What information has been gathered with regard to medication errors in the hospital? How do you use this information to improve patient safety? Provide some examples.	✓			The organization used industry standards to define medication errors; had reviewed medication data and reports, such as medication error and ADE data; and had used the data to initiate specific improvements in processes.
[4] What are the risk points in your medication management process or system? What processes were used to determine these risk points?	✓			Leaders demonstrated knowledge about the medication management system through collaborative relationships between medical staff, nursing, risk management, the pharmacy, and other departments.

(continued)

Interview Subject: Leaders (continued)

Questions	Correct Answer	Incorrect Answer	Follow-Up Needed	Comments or Notes
[5] How does the hospital evaluate medication risks and high-alert medications in particular?		✓	Need to establish a defined source list for high-alert medications, with emphasis on distribution and updating of the list.	Leaders were divided about the preferred source list for identifying high-alert medications, with some referring to the Institute for Safe Medication Practices list, whereas others used that combined with current literature.

Interview Subject: Nursing Unit Staff

Questions	Correct Answer	Incorrect Answer	Follow-Up Needed	Comments or Notes
[6] How do you ensure that you are administering a medication preparation to the correct patient?	✓			Nurses were aware of the need to follow the current National Patient Safety Goal regarding two patient identifiers prior to medication administration.
[7] Do you use the same standardized approach (pounds or kilograms) for all patients in determining the weight scheduling of their medication? How often is each patient's weight record updated?	✓			
[8] How do you work with the pharmacy and the physician when questions or concerns arise?	✓			Nurses were able to provide several examples of having a good working relationship with the pharmacy.
[9] How do you ensure that you are administering the infusion at the correct rate?	✓			
[10] What are the elements of your checking process when it comes to correct admixtures?	✓			

Interview Subject: *Nursing Unit Staff (Continued)*

Questions	Correct Answer	Incorrect Answer	Follow-Up Needed	Comments or Notes
[11] What is organization policy regarding the use of PPE during chemotherapy administration?		✓	*Organization should review training and competency related to use of PPE by nurses during chemotherapy preparation and administration.*	
[12] How are nurses who work in this area trained and deemed competent for the administration of chemotherapy medications? Of what does training consist? How is competency assessed? Please show documentation of this assessment.		✓	*Organization should review training and orientation as well as competency by nurses in all areas of chemotherapy preparation and administration.*	

Interview Subject: *Medication Room Nurse*

Questions	Correct Answer	Incorrect Answer	Follow-Up Needed	Comments or Notes
[13] What is the policy regarding returns of medication to the pharmacy?	✓		*Need to review the policy on return of medications, especially regarding chemotherapy IVs.*	*Although the nurse was following hospital policy regarding leaving discontinued IV orders on the unit, she was unaware that this constituted a danger.*
[14] How do you dispose of chemotherapy waste?	✓			
[15] How are nurses who work in this area trained and deemed competent for the administration of chemotherapy medications? Of what does training consist? How is competency assessed? Please show documentation of this assessment.	✓		*Organization should review training and orientation as well as competency by nurses in all areas of chemotherapy preparation and administration.*	
[16] Where are the nearest spill kits located? What does a kit contain? What are the procedures regarding use of the kit?	✓			

(continued)

Interview Subject: *Pharmacist*

Questions	Correct Answer	Incorrect Answer	Follow-Up Needed	Comments or Notes
[17] What part do you play in making sure chemotherapy is used safely in this organization?	✓			
[18] Where are chemotherapy medications stored and prepared? How do you address safety issues associated with storage and preparation of chemotherapy medications?	✓			
[19] What steps do you take to ensure that preparation of chemotherapy drugs is done as safely as possible?	✓			
[20] Who oversees the process to ensure that there is consistency in meeting safe practice requirements?		✓	*Copies of the protocol should be included to provide opportunity for order cross-checking.*	*Pharmacist did not include copies of the chemotherapy protocol with the order.*
[21] What are your training and competencies for the job that you do?		✓	*Review pharmacist ordering to check that all relevant as well as helpful information is present in chemotherapy orders.*	

Tracer Scenarios for
AMBULATORY CARE AND
OFFICE-BASED SURGERY

NOTE: No Two Tracers Are the Same

Please keep in mind that each tracer is unique. There is no way to know all of the questions that might be asked or documents that might be reviewed during a tracer—or what all the responses to the questions and documents might be. The possibilities are limitless, depending on the tracer topic and the organization's circumstances. These tracer scenarios and sample questions are provided as educational or training tools for organization staff; they are not scripts for real or mock tracers.

Section Elements

This section includes sample tracers—called scenarios—relevant to ambulatory care and office-based surgery. The section is organized as follows:

Scenarios: Each scenario presents what might happen when a surveyor conducts a specific type of tracer. The scenarios are presented in an engaging narrative format in which the reader "follows" the surveyor through the tracer scenario. Within the narrative are bracketed numbers that correspond to numbered sample tracer questions following the tracer.

Sample Tracer Questions: After each scenario narrative is a list of sample questions a surveyor might ask during that scenario. These questions can be used to develop and conduct mock tracers in your organization on topics similar to those covered in the scenario.

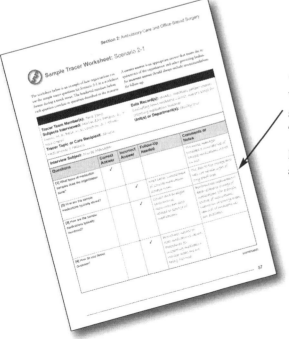

Sample Tracer Worksheet: At the end of the section is a sample worksheet that shows how the sample tracer questions for one select scenario in the section might be used in a worksheet format. The example shows how the worksheet might be completed as part of a tracer for that scenario. A blank form of the worksheet is available in Appendix B.

SCENARIO 2-1. Ambulatory Care Center

Summary

In the following scenario, the surveyor conducted a medication management system tracer at a midsized ambulatory care center. Within the tracer, the surveyor explored issues relating to these priority focus areas:

- Medication Management
- Assessment and Care/Services
- Communication
- Information Management
- Organizational Structure
- Physical Environment

Scenario

During a tour of the facility with members of staff responsible for medication storage and preparation, the surveyor learned about the care center's procedures and policies. She asked staff to describe the path medications take from delivery into the facility to storage to preparation and dispensing. As the tour progressed, the surveyor observed staff members distributing sample medications to patients. She decided to use this as a starting point for the medication management tracer.

(Bracketed numbers correlate to Sample Tracer Questions on page 44.)

➡ *Touring with the Nurse Manager.* Early in the tour, the surveyor noticed that sample medications were stored in a room that was visible from the patient waiting area but not within the line of sight of any staff area. [1–3] The door to this sample medication storage room was neither closed nor secured during the 20 minutes the surveyor was able to observe the area. Since the nurse manager was participating in the tour, the surveyor asked her about it. The manager said that the door was usually closed at all times, but acknowledged that it was indeed open at that moment. She said that staff were aware of this issue and had been directed to be mindful of it but that the problem persisted. She further acknowledged that patients had occasionally been found in the room. [4]

The surveyor continued to explore medication management processes with the nurse manager, asking about patient education on new medications, including sample medications, [5] as well as about information patients provide upon checking into the center regarding current medications. [6] The surveyor asked how medication reconciliation and administration is

documented in the patient record to ensure that the process is accurate and complete. [7–8] The nurse manager detailed the clinic's policy, pointing out that all documentation takes place in real time in the electronic medication administration record (eMAR). She then produced a checklist distributed by nursing management titled, "If It Wasn't Documented, It Wasn't Done." The checklist featured "The Five W's":

- When (time)?
- Why (including assessment, symptoms/complaints, and lab values)?
- What (medication, dose, and route)?
- Where (site)?
- Was (the medication tolerated and effective)?

➡ *Patient Interviews.* At the conclusion of the tour, the surveyor was able to interview five patients. She first reviewed each of their clinical records and found that four of the records were incomplete and inaccurate. Problems included an inaccurate home medication list in one record and incomplete pain assessments in the other four.

"Do you maintain a list of all the medications you are taking?" the surveyor asked one patient a short time later. [9–10] "Yes, I write it down so I can keep track of everything," the patient replied, producing a card and showing it to the surveyor. This same question was asked of each patient, with the same result. All five patients also indicated that they had been encouraged by staff to monitor their medications on their own. [11]

➡ *Talking with a Frontline Nurse.* The surveyor followed up her patient visits by asking a nurse to describe the organization's policy regarding sample medications. [12] She also asked him to share his understanding of the procedures regarding the storage and possible security risks of unsecured sample medications. He shared details of the policy and commented on his knowledge of the unsecured door to the sample room, adding that he was aware of recent mandates from management to keep the door closed and locked. "We follow the rule for a few weeks," he admitted. "Then we just start getting forgetful." [13–14]

The surveyor then asked the nurse to explain how he obtained medication histories. [15] The nurse said that he followed organization policy requiring the use of open-ended questions. "We're not supposed to ask questions that can be answered with just a 'yes' or 'no,'" the nurse explained. He added that creating accurate medication profiles was difficult because many of the ambulatory care center's patients were poor historians. The surveyor was also told that the organization had created a one-page script that nurses were directed to use in collecting medication histories. Nurses were also supposed to contact a patient's pharmacy if that patient was unable to remember his or her medications.

→ *Moving Forward.* Based on the tracer, the surveyor may discuss the following in the Daily Briefing: improving security for sample medications (including limiting access to designated, authorized staff; labeling of samples; consistency of distribution paths for samples; clear procedures regarding who signs for and logs in receipt of samples; potential for use of a process map or a similar tool to identify and reduce or eliminate areas of failure related to medication reconciliation.

Scenario 2-1.
Sample Tracer Questions

The bracketed numbers before each question correlate to questions, observations, and data review described in the sample tracer for Scenario 2-1. You can use the tracer worksheet form in Appendix B to develop a mock tracer (*see* an example of a completed tracer worksheet at the end of this section). The information gained by conducting a mock tracer can help to highlight a good practice and/or determine issues that may require further follow-up.

Nurse Manager:

[1] What types of medication samples does the organization store?

[2] How are the sample medications typically stored?

[3] How are the sample medications typically monitored?

[4] How do you detect diversion?

[5] What education do patients receive when being provided with sample medications? Are written instructions provided?

[6] What is the process for collecting medication information from the patients? Who is responsible for collecting the information?

[7] Is this information compiled and reconciled at each visit? What department is responsible for reconciling the information?

[8] Are patients encouraged to maintain a medication profile and to bring it to each clinic visit?

Patients:

[9] Do you maintain a list of all the medications you are taking? Explain why you think having this list if a good idea.

[10] Do you bring the list with you to all clinic visits?

[11] Have you received education regarding the proper use of your medications?

Frontline Nurse:

[12] What issues have been identified regarding control, labeling, security, and documentation of sample medications?

[13] Has patient access to sample medications been identified as a safety risk, and if so, what has been done to minimize this risk?

[14] What improvements have been implemented to correct any problems related to management of sample medications?

[15] Explain the process used to obtain accurate and complete medication histories from patients. How do you know that this process is being carried out?

SCENARIO 2-2. Office-Based Surgery Practice

Summary

In the following scenario, a surveyor conducted a medication management system tracer at an office-based surgery practice. Within the tracer, the surveyor explored issues relating to these priority focus areas:
- Medication Management
- Credentialed Practitioners
- Information Management
- Orientation & Training
- Patient Safety

Scenario

The surveyor conducted this medication management tracer in an office-based surgery practice. He first met with both the practice owner and the performance improvement (PI) coordinator to review the practice's medication-related policies. After this, the plan was for the surveyor to tour a procedural area with the owner, followed by a visit to the organization's records room with the PI coordinator.

(Bracketed numbers correlate to Sample Tracer Questions on page 45–46.)

→ *Touring the Procedural Area.* Later, the surveyor was escorted by the practice owner to a small surgical area, where the surveyor donned proper garbing to observe the performance of a procedure. He noticed the presence of unlabeled medicine containers in the operating suite despite the requirements spelled out in National Patient Safety Goal NPSG.03.04.01 (*see* Appendix E, page 152). [1] In addition, those containers that were labeled included only the name of the medication and were missing strength-and date-related information. When the surveyor asked about this, the owner called over the nurse on duty who pointed out that the containers followed organization policy. [2] Despite this, the surveyor reminded her of a labeling policy he had read during his initial meeting that required all containers to include the medication name, volume, and strength. [3]

The surveyor then asked the same nurse whether and how she performed a presurgical verification process. The nurse described the process, showed him a checklist, and explained the marking of the surgical site. The surveyor remained in the operating suite long enough to observe the time-out—a Universal Protocol requirement (*see* Appendix E, page 154)—prior to the start of the procedure, [4] before moving on to the records room.

→ *Touring the Records Room.* In the organization's records room with the PI coordinator, the surveyor examined 10 records and noticed many instances of abbreviations and symbols that he had seen earlier on the organization's do-not-use list. [5] Specifically, he saw that "MS" was used as an abbreviation for morphine sulfate in more than one case, and noted that in many cases, there were no leading zeros before decimals for medications dosed in fractional amounts.

When he pointed this out to a physician that happened to be in the room at that time, the physician said that he was aware of the organization's do-not-use list but did not think that this policy applied to surgery/procedural reports. He assumed the list applied only to the writing of prescriptions. [6]

→ *With the PI Coordinator.* Returning to the PI coordinator's office, the surveyor shared what he had learned in the records room. The coordinator responded by explaining that the organization had zero tolerance for the use of any abbreviations or symbols found on its do-not-use list. She said that information regarding restrictions on the use of specific symbols and abbreviations was included in the orientation and training materials received by all staff involved in the medication and ordering process. [7] Further, abbreviations and symbols on the list had been removed from preprinted documentation.

The surveyor asked how the organization tracked compliance with the organization's policies on the topic, [8] and the coordinator said that the practice owner talked one-on-one with physicians when unacceptable abbreviations or symbols were brought to his attention. [9] This process, she added, was conducted informally, and she was not aware of any documentation of those conversations. [10–11]

→ *Moving Forward.* Based on the tracer, the surveyor may discuss the following in the Daily Briefing: the regular review of open medical records to help ensure that do-not-use abbreviations and symbols were not being used; auditing closed records to assess compliance with the organization's policies; formally documenting continued noncompliance in physicians' credentials files; labeling for all medications and solutions; investigating methods of ensuring that original containers from medications or solutions remain available in the perioperative area until a procedure is completed.

Scenario 2-2.
Sample Tracer Questions

The bracketed numbers before each question correlate to questions, observations, and data review described in the sample tracer for Scenario 2-2. You can use the tracer worksheet form in Appendix B to develop a mock tracer (*see* an example of a completed tracer worksheet at the end of this section). The information gained by conducting a mock tracer can help to highlight a good practice and/or determine issues that may require further follow-up.

Practice Owner and Procedural Area Nurse:

[1] What is the process for labeling containers in the procedural field? Who is responsible for doing it?

[2] Are all containers labeled in the manner defined by policy?

[3] What is the sequence for the labeling these containers?

[4] Has the practice adopted the requirements of the Universal Protocol for Preventing Wrong Site, Wrong Procedure, and Wrong Person Surgery™ as policy and incorporated it as part of its surgical procedures? Explain how the organization complies with the Universal Protocol.

PI Coordinator and Physician:

[5] Does the organization have a list of unapproved abbreviations?

[6] What training have you had regarding the use of these unapproved abbreviations?

[7] What education is provided for staff regarding the use of do-not-use abbreviations?

(continued)

Scenario 2-2.
Sample Tracer Questions (continued)

[8] How is the use of do-not-use abbreviations monitored in the organization?

[9] Are data on the use of do-not-use abbreviations incorporated into the credentialing and privileging process? What possible trends can you spot in your data?

[10] What actions are taken if someone in the organization detects the use of do-not-use abbreviations?

[11] Are actions related to use of do-not-use abbreviations documented?

SCENARIO 2-3. Large Ambulatory Care Center

Summary

In the following scenario, a surveyor conducted a medication management tracer at a large ambulatory care center. Within the tracer, the surveyor explored issues relating to these priority focus areas:

- Medication Management
- Patient Safety
- Communication
- Information Management

Scenario

The surveyor was in a large ambulatory care center that provided emergency services, laboratory and radiology services, cardiac and pulmonary rehabilitation and support services, and infusion for chemotherapy patients. The surveyor learned that all of these services were supported by an on-site pharmacy. The surveyor decided to examine chemotherapy infusion during this medication management tracer.

(Bracketed numbers correlate to Sample Tracer Questions on page 47.)

➡ *Speaking to a Nurse.* The surveyor pulled the record of a patient being treated for colon cancer and spoke first with the nurse who cared care for this particular patient. The patient was scheduled to arrive later in the day, and the surveyor wanted to follow aspects of medication management through her experience. The surveyor reviewed the medication orders with the nurse, asking him about the patient and the prescribed medication regimen in an effort to get an understanding of the organization's medication management processes. [1–2] The surveyor and nurse reviewed the medication order and discussed the organization's overall processes for storage, dispensing, preparing, administering, and monitoring of the medications needed by the colon cancer patient.

The surveyor asked what the nurse would do if he received orders that included abbreviations not permitted by organization policy. The nurse said he didn't recall any problems with the use of unapproved abbreviations for medications for this particular patient but that a recent in-service training session focused on how nurses could more effectively speak up to get clarifications on medication orders.

The surveyor asked the nurse how chemotherapy orders were calculated. [3] The nurse said that organization policy called for weight-based dosing for all chemotherapy drugs. The surveyor noted that the prescription for the colon cancer patient was clear and legible and that it spelled out the weight-based dosing calculation. The nurse said he typically transcribes the order on the medication administration record (MAR) after bringing in a second nurse. This is necessary to complete the two-nurse check required by the organization. Orders are then sent to the pharmacy.

➡ *In the On-Site Pharmacy.* The surveyor then moved on to the pharmacy, where he asked the pharmacist to explain the process for reviewing the appropriateness of orders. [4] All orders are prepared by the pharmacy and sent to the unit. The pharmacist showed the surveyor how a pharmacy technician screens all orders and enters them into a computer system. The pharmacist then reviews the original order and verifies the technician's entry in the computer. [5]

The surveyor asked the pharmacy technician to show her how investigational medications were stored in the pharmacy and then observed the technician preparing a chemotherapy order. [6] The technician followed garbing procedures, including donning a mask and gloves. [7–8] The surveyor finished by asking the technician to explain the disposal process for hazardous materials. [9]

➡ *Back with the Nurse.* The surveyor returned to the patient care area to observe the administration of the chemotherapy infusion for the colon cancer patient. The nurse, who was dressed in a gown and two sets of gloves, one of which were approved for use with chemotherapy, prepared to hang the bag of chemotherapy medication, but first conducted a check on the infusion pump with another nurse. Per policy, one of the nurses set the rate in the pump and the other confirmed that it had been done properly. **[10]** The pair checked the patient's name, medical record number, drug(s), dose, route, date and time, solution, and expiration date against the medical record. The nurse explained to the surveyor that organization policy required this check.

After the infusion had been administered, the surveyor asked if the nurse had ever had a chemotherapy infusion fall and split open. **[11]** The nurse said it had happened and that a chemotherapy spill kit must be used in such instances. The nurse showed the surveyor a spill kit, which contained items such as a gown, gloves, goggles, and absorbent spill pillows. The nurse said he would use the spill pillows to wipe up the spill and then use the bags in the spill kit to seal up all the contaminated items. He said that nurses were required to alert a supervisor when a spill occurs.

➜ *Moving Forward.* Based on the tracer, the surveyor may discuss the following in the Daily Briefing: nurse competencies related to chemotherapy infusion and safe handling of hazardous materials.

Scenario 2-3.
Sample Tracer Questions

The bracketed numbers before each question correlate to questions, observations, and data review described in the sample tracer for Scenario 2-3. You can use the tracer worksheet form in Appendix B to develop a mock tracer (*see* an example of a completed tracer worksheet at the end of this section). The information gained by conducting a mock tracer can help to highlight a good practice and/or determine issues that may require further follow-up.

Nurse:
[1] What medications are being administered to this patient at the ambulatory care center?

[2] What process do you follow to administer new orders?

[3] Show me the process for obtaining the chemotherapy infusion.

Pharmacy Staff:
[4] What steps do you take in reviewing the appropriateness of orders?

[5] What are the processes the pharmacy performs to review an order and then dispense it?

[6] How do you prepare chemotherapy medications?

[7] Are special precautions used to prepare chemotherapy medications?

[8] What training have you received related to hazardous materials?

[9] How do you dispose of chemotherapy medications?

Nurse:
[10] What, if any, precautions are required before administration? What is organization policy regarding the use of personal protective equipment during chemotherapy administration?

[11] What training have you received relative to chemotherapy? What action would you take if a chemotherapy infusion spilled?

SCENARIO 2-4. Ambulatory Surgery Center

Summary
In the following scenario, a surveyor conducted a medication management tracer at an ambulatory surgery center. Within the tracer, the surveyor explored issues relating to these priority focus areas:
- Medication Management
- Patient Safety
- Quality Improvement Expertise/Activities

Scenario
This medication management system tracer took place in an ambulatory surgery center that performed a variety of outpatient procedures. The surveyor met with the organization's leadership—the nursing leader and quality improvement coordinator. Afterwards, the surveyor decided to trace a patient who had surgery earlier in the day.

(Bracketed numbers correlate to Sample Tracer Questions on page 48.)

➜ *Nursing and Pain Relief Orders.* The surveyor asked the nursing leader to explain how care staff had received postoperative medication administration orders for the selected patient. **[1]** The nursing leader introduced the surveyor to this patient's nurse, who showed the surveyor the orders. On it, the surgeon had written that the patient "should receive pain re-lief" and had listed an analgesic to be administered. [2–3] The surveyor asked the nurse how he would know what dose to ad-minister since it was not specified on the order. [4] The nurse said he had worked with this surgeon for a number of years and "just knew," adding that he had never had a problem con-tacting that particular surgeon to get clarification on an order when he needed it. [5–6]

→ *With the Quality Improvement Coordinator.* The surveyor decided to follow up on the conversation with the nurse about pain relief orders. She asked the quality improve-ment coordinator about medication safety in relation to or-ders, including any policies and processes for ensuring clear and legible orders. [7–9] The coordinator explained that the organization performed chart audits to identify deviations from policies on medication ordering and that staff and physi-cians were educated about organization expectations and poli-cies. The coordinator showed the surveyor the audit form, which included a series of questions that should be answered "yes," "no," or "incomplete." A section on corrective actions was required for each "no" or "incomplete" answer. The audit included questions such as "Are the medication orders clear re-garding dose to be given?" and "Are the medication orders clear regarding time to be given?"

The surveyor then asked the coordinator what kinds of data were collected regarding the medication management process and medication errors. [10] She also asked what analysis and resulting improvements had been made based on that data col-lection. [11–12] The quality improvement coordinator ex-plained that the organization recently discovered some near misses and medication errors due to inconsistently labeled medications. As a result, the organization improved its labeling process and began requiring the use of color-coded labels and a larger type size on the labels. Data collection after the change had shown a reduction in medication errors related to labeling. [13]

→ *Moving Forward.* Based on the tracer, the surveyor may discuss the following in the Daily Briefing: placing greater em-phasis on ensuring complete medication orders (the open-ended pain relief medication order presented risks), including working with prescribers to ensure that all orders include a dosage range and a stated time period; examining how the or-ganization conducts pain assessments and training that nurses receive related to conducting and using pain assessments.

Scenario 2-4.
Sample Tracer Questions

The bracketed numbers before each question correlate to questions, observations, and data review described in the sample tracer for Scenario 2-4. You can use the tracer worksheet form in Appendix B to develop a mock tracer (*see* an example of a completed tracer worksheet at the end of this section). The information gained by conducting a mock tracer can help to highlight a good practice and/or determine issues that may require further follow-up.

Nurse:

[1] What is your organization's process for receiving medication orders?

[2] What types of medications are usually prescribed in this unit or department?

[3] What do you do if a medication order is illegible or unclear?

[4] What is your organization's process for administering medications?

[5] What is the organization's process for approaching the prescribing physician about a concern or a question about a medication order?

[6] What is the center's policy regarding the details of medication administration orders? If so, how is the policy monitored? How is it enforced?

Quality Improvement Coordinator:

[7] Do you have a policy that addresses the required components for all types of medication orders?

[8] What education and training do you provide to staff regarding medication safety and issues related to high-alert medications?

[9] What policies and processes do you have related to medication orders that are illegible or unclear?

[10] What type of data do you collect regarding medication management?

[11] How do you analyze the data collected regarding medication management?

[12] How are the data results reported?

[13] What kinds of improvements have been made as a result of data analysis?

SCENARIO 2-5. Community-Based, Federally Qualified Health Center

Summary

In the following scenario, a surveyor conducted a medication management system tracer at a community-based, federally qualified health center. Within the tracer, the surveyor explored issues relating to these priority focus areas:

- Medication Management
- Leadership and Planning
- Patient and Family Education

Note: *Federally qualified community health centers are community-based and patient-directed organizations that serve populations with limited access to health care. Typically, they serve low-income populations, the uninsured, those with limited English proficiency, and migrant and seasonal farm workers, as well as individuals and families experiencing homelessness or living in public housing.*

Scenario

This tracer began with a meeting attended by the surveyor and key staff involved in the organization's medication management system. The surveyor was seeking information about the organization's medication management processes, from planning and procurement of medications through monitoring, if applicable, and the medication reconciliation process during handoffs from one level of care to another in cases involving medication prescription.

(Bracketed numbers correlate to Sample Tracer Questions on page 50.)

➡ *Interviewing Leaders.* In reviewing the services provided by the organization, the surveyor asked two leaders—the performance improvement (PI) director and the nursing leader—to describe the scope of medication services provided by the organization. [1] These leaders told the surveyor that the scope of medication services in the organization was limited to immunizations, emergency medications, and sample medications for indigent patients. [2] The surveyor asked the leaders to explain the requirements for safe storage of immunizations in refrigerators and freezers and how the requirements were determined. [3–5] The leaders cited appropriate guidelines from the state health department. They also said that immunizations were administered according to protocol and that physicians and nurses were available with recovery

medications in case an adverse reaction occurred. The surveyor finished the opening portion of the tracer with a few questions about how the center handled data collection regarding its medication management efforts—including frequency, how resulting analyses was shared, and how the results were used to make improvements in the processes. [6–9]

Switching topics, the surveyor then asked the two leaders to identify a risk point in the system. They explained that the organization conducted informal reviews, particularly on the storage of immunizations, but did not document the evaluation process. They added that documentation of the review was not a requirement according to Joint Commission standards. This response prompted the surveyor to request and review 10 records of patients who had received vaccinations. He noted that documentation of the administration route was not included in 3 of the records even though organization policy required documentation of route, site, and date of administration.

➡ *Talking with Nurses.* Next, to follow up on his review of medication management policies the surveyor visited the immunization areas to observe actual practice. He talked to nurses about who could administer immunizations and how this process was supervised.

"What elements must be documented for each vaccine given?" the surveyor asked a nurse who had just given an influenza immunization. [10] The nurse confirmed what the surveyor learned from his previous discussion.

The surveyor observed that staff attempted to obtain and document patient allergy information quite well. [11] There seemed to be some difficulties with medication reconciliation, however, particularly in regard to understanding whether a patient was getting and taking his or her medications. Sometimes, a nurse explained, patients did not like to admit that they were not following instructions. Other times, they seemed to fear that admitting that they did not understand medication instructions would cause staff to think less of them. [12–13]

The surveyor asked another nurse what medications were available on site. [14] The nurse said that there was no pharmacy on site. Patients took prescriptions written by the clinic's physicians and nurse practitioners to the pharmacy of their choice. She said that some sample medications, provided by drug company representatives, were stored at the clinic. [15] The surveyor then discussed with the nurses the policies and procedures for handling and storing sample medications. The surveyor asked still another nurse to show him where samples were kept. In the sample storage area, the surveyor found that some sample medications were beyond their expiration dates. The surveyor asked the nurse about the process for disposal of sample medications and for ensuring proper storage temperature for sample medications. **[16–18]** The nurse replied that she was not familiar with that aspect of the medication management process.

The surveyor then asked the nurse for information about medications that have been problematic in the organization. She said that the organization had undertaken an initiative to improve patient safety with regard to medication use. **[19]** The initiative, sponsored by the Health Resources and Services Administration (HRSA), sought to provide better patient education regarding medication use by increasing collaboration with pharmacies and/or by having a clinical pharmacy integrated within the organization. The nurse told the surveyor that language and cultural issues were important considerations in developing strong patient and provider relationships that support improved care. **[20]**

➜ *Moving Forward.* Based on the tracer, the surveyor may discuss the following in the Daily Briefing: better monitoring of compliance and analysis to determine the reasons for noncompliance; implementation of more formal documentation of processes related to risk assessment; tighter controls on documenting the sample medications given to patients as well as a review of who is allowed to distribute sample medications.

Scenario 2-5.
Sample Tracer Questions

The bracketed numbers before each question correlate to questions, observations, and data review described in the sample tracer for Scenario 2-5. You can use the tracer worksheet form in Appendix B to develop a mock tracer (*see* an example of a completed tracer worksheet at the end of this section). The information gained by conducting a mock tracer can help to highlight a good practice and/or determine issues that may require further follow-up.

PI Director and Nursing Leader:

[1] How does the organization's medication management process work?

[2] What types of medications are usually administered in the clinic?

[3] What are the organization's policy and process for storage of medication?

[4] What is the organization's policy or procedure for ensuring that medications are properly stored?

[5] What happens when the organization discovers that medications are not being stored properly?

[6] What type of data do you collect regarding medication management?

[7] How frequently do you collect these data?

[8] How are the data results analyzed and reported?

[9] What kinds of improvements have been made as a result of data analysis?

Nurses:

[10] What is the required documentation for each vaccine given?

[11] What types of information do you collect from patients about their medication history?

[12] How does the organization track whether patients fill their prescriptions and take their medications?

[13] How do you educate patients about medications you are administering?

[14] What types of medications are available on site?

[15] Do you know if the organization has policies regarding sample medications? Where are sample medications stored?

[16] Explain how you handle sample medications—from storage to security to distribution to patients.

[17] What is the required temperature for the medication storage room or area? What is organization policy for expired medications?

[18] Are there special requirements for refrigeration temperature documentation for vaccines?

[19] How are you involved in PI activities? Provide an example of a medication that has been problematic.

[20] How does your organization address language and cultural issues?

SCENARIO 2-6. Plastic Surgery Center

Summary

In the following scenario, a surveyor conducted a medication management system tracer at a plastic surgery center. Within the tracer, the surveyor explored issues relating to these priority focus areas:

- Medication Management
- Patient Safety

Scenario

The surveyor conducted a medication management tracer at a plastic surgery center that performed a variety of procedures, such as liposuction, breast augmentation, rhinoplasty, and blepharoplasty. During the opening conference, the surveyor met with the center's medical director, nurse manager, and certified registered nurse anesthetist (CRNA).

(Bracketed numbers correlate to Sample Tracer Questions on page 52.)

➜ *Meeting with Leaders.* After introductions, the surveyor and leadership staff discussed the center's medication management and medication safety practices. [1] Specifically, the session addressed the organization's activities surrounding the labeling of medication containers, how process medication management improvements were incorporated, and how new processes were monitored. The surveyor also learned how the organization collected information regarding medication errors and how the information was analyzed and used to improve patient safety. [2–4] The CRNA advised that general anesthesia is administered for some procedures. [5] By the end of this opening conference, the surveyor had decided to focus the tracer on the center's policies and procedures regarding medication labeling and high-alert medications.

➜ *With the Nurse Manager.* Later, in a meeting with the nurse manager, the surveyor asked to see a list of high-alert medications specific to the center. [6] The nurse manager complied, saying that a small work group, including the director and CRNA, had developed the list by reviewing expert literature and Joint Commission requirements. The written list included neuromuscular blockers. [7]

When asked how the center worked to avoid medication errors related to anesthesia, the nurse manager said that a literature review of common anesthesia-related adverse events had led to the

development and implementation of numerous safety processes. For examples, nurses are required to perform two checks of a medicine's name against the prescribed name and two checks of the actual dose against the prescribed dosage. For patient-controlled analgesia pumps, she continued, each programmed parameter (analgesic name, bolus dose, lockout interval, dose limit, and background infusion rate) must be checked twice. Vials of liquid drugs are labeled with the total weight of the drug and the total volume of liquid in the vial. The manager said that there were also charts available that showed precalculated doses versus weights for various medicines to avoid calculation errors. [8]

➜ *Discussing Error Prevention with Staff.* After gathering information with the nurse manager, the surveyor toured the facility and talked with two nurses on duty about strategies to prevent the accidental administration of neuromuscular blockers. [9] By way of example, one of the nurses showed the surveyor a special refrigerator for the exclusive use of the CRNA. Inside, the medications were in a bin clearly marked with a label reading "neuromuscular blockers." Access to the refrigerator was limited and monitored. [10]

When questioned about their training on the potential for medication mistakes, the second nurse told the surveyor that all nurses on staff had received training in this regard. In particular, she mentioned training about errors related to neuromuscular blockers for patients who are not intubated. The nurse added that she was aware of the center's policies regarding special handling of these drugs and that, upon receipt, neuromuscular blockers were to be brought to the CRNA refrigerator immediately and placed in the special bin. The surveyor made a note to check with the nurse manager later to determine when nurses received training to handle this task and what criteria is used to develop the training curriculum.

A short time later, the surveyor was able to observe the labeling of medications and solutions that had been removed from their original containers. She checked whether every medication in a cup was labeled with appropriate information, either just prior to or just after the medication was placed into the container. [11] One of the nurses pointed out that organization policy did not allow for prelabeling of containers. The surveyor asked the two nurses she spoke with during the tour for an example of an error or near miss and how that event had been used to understand the causes of system breakdowns better, as well as to improve processes. They immediately explained that the process the surveyor had just observed for segregating neuromuscular blockers was created after a refrigerator was mistakenly stocked with a paralyzing agent. [12]

→ *Moving Forward.* Based on the tracer, the surveyor most likely found no significant problem areas to address in the Daily Briefing.

Scenario 2-6.
Sample Tracer Questions

The bracketed numbers before each question correlate to questions, observations, and data review described in the sample tracer for Scenario 2-6. You can use the tracer worksheet form in Appendix B to develop a mock tracer (*see* an example of a completed tracer worksheet at the end of this section). The information gained by conducting a mock tracer can help to highlight a good practice and/or determine issues that may require further follow-up.

Leaders:

[1]   How do you evaluate the effectiveness of your medication management system?

[2]   How do you improve the safety of using your medications? Explain how look-alike/sound-alike medications are managed and how you address the labeling of medication containers.

[3]   How do you address the need for staff to improve the safety of using medications?

[4]   Are staff involved with performance improvement processes related to identified errors and near misses? How are they involved?

[5]   Describe any processes in place to prevent anesthesia-related errors.

Nurse Manager:

[6]   How has the organization addressed risks associated with high-alert medications?

[7]   What specific high-alert drug is most commonly used at your organization?

[8]   What steps have been taken to avoid anesthesia-related errors? Provide examples of some of the steps.

Staff:

[9]   Describe any training or competency assessments related to medication safety strategies.

[10]   How are medication containers labeled when medications are prepared but not immediately administered?

[11]   Provide an example of an everyday medication safety step you perform that explicitly adheres to your organization's medication safety policy.

[12]   Are you involved with performance improvement processes related to identified errors and near misses? How have you been involved?

SCENARIO 2-7. Hospital-Based Family Practice Primary Care Facility

Summary

In the following scenario, a surveyor conducted a medication management tracer at a hospital-based family practice primary care facility. Within the tracer, the surveyor explored issues relating to these priority focus areas:

- Medication Management
- Organizational Structure
- Informational Management
- Assessment and Care/Services
- Patient Safety

Scenario

The surveyor conducted a medication management system tracer in a hospital-based family practice primary care facility. All of the family practice physicians on staff at this facility, which was located near the border of two states, also had privileges at a hospital located approximately 10 miles across the state line. This situation prompted the surveyor to investigate staff involvement in performance improvement (PI) for the facility.

(Bracketed numbers correlate to Sample Tracer Questions on page 53.)

→ *With the Medical Director.* The surveyor asked to meet with the medical director to discuss staff involvement in PI for this facility in regard to medication management systems. The medical director, in his dual role as the practice's PI coordinator, first addressed how prescriber licensure were verified and documented. [1] Most licenses, he explained, were verified through primary source verification, where the verification of a current license was obtained from the body that issued the license. [2] The director then summarized the practice's medication management processes and the responsibilities the licensed prescribers had in not only adhering to policies, but contributing to improvements to the policies as well. [3–4]

Turning his focus to an individual medication-related topic involving credentialed staff, the surveyor asked the director about the process employed to ensure clear and legible medication orders. The director said the organization performed frequent record audits to determine if there were any unwanted issues with orders. Regardless of the results, these audits were usually followed by an effort to reiterate and reinforce organization expectations and policy in regard to writing orders. [5] When the surveyor was finished talking with the medical director, he decided to interview nursing staff.

➡ *With Nursing Staff.* When the surveyor asked nursing staff about adherence to the organization's medication ordering policy, they agreed that there were absolutely no problems with the credentialed and privileged physicians they worked with. However, they indicated that the facility received orders for patients' medications from many sources, including community physicians who were not credentialed and privileged by the hospital clinic. The clinic did not have a method of verifying the licensure of those physicians. [6–9]

➡ *With Credentialling Staff.* Later, the surveyor reviewed the privileging records of some of the credentialing staff, as well as some patient records. In doing so, he confirmed the nurses' report that orders were occasionally received from non-privileged prescribers. [10] In addition, he discovered several incidents where physicians were working without evidence of licensure verification. When he mentioned this to members of the organization's credentialing staff, they admitted that they sometimes assumed a prescriber was licensed in the bordering state and thus had not always validated the licenses. [11–12]

➡ *Moving Forward.* Based on the tracer, the surveyor may discuss the following in the Daily Briefing: the need for a process to prevent filling medication orders from nonprivileged prescribers; the need to ensure all prescribers' licenses are verified; the need to ensure that all credentialed and privileged prescribers adhere to all medication management policies and participate in the improvement of these policies.

Scenario 2-7.
Sample Tracer Questions

The bracketed numbers before each question correlate to questions, observations, and data review described in the sample tracer for Scenario 2-7. You can use the tracer worksheet form in Appendix B to develop a mock tracer (*see* an example of a completed tracer worksheet at the end of this section). The information gained by conducting a mock tracer can help to highlight a good practice and/or determine issues that may require further follow-up.

Medical Director:

[1] What processes are in place to verify prescriber licensure? How is this process documented?

[2] How often are these prescriber licenses verified? Are the licenses verified using primary source verification?

[3] Describe your medication management process. Are all privileged staff involved in making improvements to this process? How is this handled?

[4] How does your organization ensure that its prescribers follow its policies?

[5] Provide an example of a key guideline or procedure related to your medication process and how its adherence is promoted among privileged prescribers.

Nursing Staff:

[6] Are orders accepted from nonprivileged prescribers?

[7] Is there a process to verify the licensure of nonprivileged prescribers?

[8] What is your organization's process for nurses approaching a prescribing physician with a concern or question about a medication order?

[9] Does the credentialing process verify a prescriber's licensure?

Credentialing Staff

[10] Does the organization allow nonprivileged prescribers to order medications for clinic patients?

[11] What process is used to verify the licensure of nonprivileged prescribers?

[12] Does this process require primary source verification?

SCENARIO 2-8. Community-Based Gastrointestinal Clinic

Summary

In the following scenario, a surveyor conducted a medication management system tracer at a community-based gastrointestinal clinic. Within the tracer, the surveyor explored issues relating to these priority focus areas:

- Medication Management
- Patient Safety
- Organizational Structure

Scenario

During a survey at the clinic, the surveyor noted a number of medication-related issues. These included the handling and storage of multidose drug vials and the storage and availability of the drug epinephrine on a crash cart. He had decided that he would give these situations a closer look during the medication management tracer. The surveyor got the opportunity to follow up when he made a point of revisiting specific areas with a clinic physician.

(Bracketed numbers correlate to Sample Tracer Questions on page 55.)

➡ *Touring the Clinic with a Physician.* During this tour of the clinic, the surveyor stopped at some wall cabinets located in the procedural area. He noticed punctured and opened multidose vials that were stored without new beyond-use-dates (BUDs). [1] The vials included medications such as betamethasone and lidocaine. He asked the physician giving him the tour to explain the clinic's policy for opening vials of medication and was told that it was okay to write the date the vial was opened. [2–5]

➡ *With a Nurse at the Crash Cart.* Next, the surveyor was escorted by a nurse to the crash cart the surveyor had noticed during his earlier walk around. Referring to the emergency medications on the cart, the surveyor asked the nurse why the epinephrine for injection was not in a most ready-to-administer form. [6] The nurse responded that the appropriate dosage form of the medication had not been available from the pharmacy. [7] The alternative methods for having the medication in the most ready-to-administer form just had not been explored, she admitted. [8–10]

➡ *With the Pharmacist.* Eventually, the surveyor was able to meet with the pharmacist to discuss observations made and explanations received regarding the vials in the procedural area and the epinephrine on the crash cart. [11] Despite the training provided to all new nurses at orientation, the pharmacist said expiration dates on vials remained a challenge. [12] He further explained that organization policy required multidose vials to be relabeled with a revised expiration date once the multidose vial was opened or punctured. Labeling the multidose vial with the date opened was not permitted, he added. The pharmacist also explained that when epinephrine ampoules or vials are used instead of emergency syringes, the vial, diluents, and syringe were all supposed to be labeled with the drug's name and strength, and instructions were to be included for preparing a dilution equivalent to a prefilled emergency syringe. [13–14]

➡ *Moving Forward.* Based on the tracer, the surveyor may discuss the following in the Daily Briefing: an organizational review of medication storage areas and crash carts for appropriateness and compliance with policies and procedures, as well as a review of in-service education regarding expiration dating of opened vials.

Scenario 2-8. Sample Tracer Questions

The bracketed numbers before each question correlate to questions, observations, and data review described in the sample tracer for Scenario 2-8. You can use the tracer worksheet form in Appendix B to develop a mock tracer (*see* an example of a completed tracer worksheet at the end of this section). The information gained by conducting a mock tracer can help to highlight a good practice and/or determine issues that may require further follow-up.

Clinic Physician:

[1] How can you tell if a medication is for single use or multiple dose use?

[2] What is the clinic's policy regarding the expiration dating of opened vials?

[3] Are opened multidose vials without new BUDs routinely available for use on patients?

[4] What is the correct BUD for opened multidose vials?

[5] What is the policy regarding the opening and storing of vials of medication without BUDs?

Nurse:

[6] What is the organization's policy regarding the provision of emergency medications in their most ready-to-administer forms?

[7]   What alternative methods are used to obtain emergency medications in their most ready-to-administer form if they are not commercially available?

[8]   Have you received training on applying expiration dates on opened vials?

[9]   What is the clinic's policy for emergency medication dosage forms?

[10] What are the acquisition methods for obtaining these dosage forms in the event of a shortage?

Pharmacist:

[11] Are you aware that some of these vials are replacing preloaded syringes in the crash carts?

[12] Has the pharmacy provided any staff training regarding the application of expiration dates to vials when they are opened?

[13] What is the organization policy for dispensing of dosage forms for emergency medications? What are its policies for providing adequate supplies of these medications in the event of a shortage?

[14] Does the pharmacy have the capability to prepare medication like epinephrine in the appropriate dosage forms if not available from the manufacturer?

SCENARIO 2-9. Primary Health Care Center

Summary

In the following scenario, a surveyor conducted a medication management system tracer at a primary health care center. Within the tracer, the surveyor explored issues relating to these priority focus areas:

- Medication Management
- Assessment and Care/Services

Scenario

A surveyor looked at a small primary health care center's medication management system during an individual medication management tracer. Near the end of the tracer, the surveyor met with the center's director and asked to be allowed to observe a staff member work with a patient.

(Bracketed numbers correlate to Sample Tracer Questions on page 56.)

➤ *With the Director.* The surveyor asked the director to describe the center's policy on medications and how it stored, labeled, and administered sample medications. [1–2] The director explained that samples were stored in a locked cupboard and that staff attended monthly training sessions to help them improve patient education when distributing samples. The surveyor asked the director about the center's medication reconciliation policy. [3] The director described it in detail, taking a few minutes to focus on a recent initiative that partnered staff and patients on medication safety. [4] He told the surveyor that posters in the lobby, as well as in all patient care rooms, encouraged patients to, among other actions, bring their medications to each of their appointments. In addition, he said, a reminder was included on each appointment card. Appointment-reminder phone calls also included a scripted prompt from staff reminding patients to bring medications to the clinic.

➤ *Observing a Nurse.* The surveyor then joined a nurse who was about to give an infant a vaccination. Before joining the patient, the surveyor asked the nurse to show him where the vaccines were stored. [5] The surveyor checked the labeling on the stored vaccines and was about to verify that the vaccines were properly stored and labeled when he noticed that some were not organized in a consistent manner. He also discovered a few sample medications not stored at all but left in a pile on a counter. [6] Additional questions for the nurse followed, ending with the surveyor asking if the nurse had ever needed to calculate doses for the clinic's pediatric patients. [7] She said that the pharmacy provided ready-to-administer doses.

The surveyor then accompanied the nurse into an examining room, where the infant and mother were waiting. He observed the vaccination process and watched as the nurse educated the infant's parent on post-vaccination care. [8] The nurse offered preprinted vaccination education sheets to the mother, reviewed the "Frequently Asked Questions" portion of this material, and allowed time for further questions and discussion.

➤ *Moving Forward.* Based on the tracer, the surveyor may discuss the following in the Daily Briefing: compliance with requirements regarding storage and labeling of vaccines and sample medications.

Scenario 2-9.
Sample Tracer Questions

The bracketed numbers before each question correlate to questions, observations, and data review described in the sample tracer for Scenario 2-9. You can use the tracer worksheet form in Appendix B to develop a mock tracer (*see* an example of a completed tracer worksheet at the end of this section). The information gained by conducting a mock tracer can help to highlight a good practice and/or determine issues that may require further follow-up.

Director:

[1]   Please describe organization policy regarding the storage, labeling, and administration of medication samples.

[2]   Show me where sample medications are stored. Who has access to the samples?

[3]   How do you get a complete list of the medications that a patient is taking?

[4]   What does your organization do to educate patients on medication safety?

Nurse:

[5]   Are there special requirements for the storage of vaccines at the clinic?

[6]   Show me where sample medications are typically stored. What is the organization's normal procedure on storage and handling of sample medications?

[7]   How are medications for pediatric patients prepared?

[8]   How do you educate patients about their medications?

Sample Tracer Worksheet: Scenario 2-1.

The worksheet below is an example of how organizations can use the sample tracer questions for Scenario 2-1 in a worksheet format during a mock tracer. The bracketed numbers before each question correlate to questions described in the scenario.

A **correct answer** is an appropriate answer that meets the requirements of the organization and other governing bodies. An **incorrect answer** should always include recommendations for follow-up.

Tracer Team Member(s): Terra Yang
Subjects Interviewed: Marion Zho, Patients (L. T. Duran, M. K. Palla, N. R. Woodrow, S. I. Olive), Nero Caponi
Tracer Topic or Care Recipient: Sample Medications; 5 Patients

Data Record(s): eMARs, checklist, patient records (including home medication lists), nurse's script for collecting medication histories
Unit(s) or Department(s): facility tour

Interview Subject: Nurse Manager

Questions	Correct Answer	Incorrect Answer	Follow-Up Needed	Comments or Notes
[1] What types of medication samples does the organization store?	✓			The nurse manager provided a complete list of sample medications stored on site.
[2] How are the sample medications typically stored?		✓	Need better surveillance of sample medication storage room.	The door to the storage area was not within sight of any staff area.
[3] How are the sample medications typically monitored?		✓	Collect and analyze performance measurement data related to storage of medications.	Performance measurement data related to storage of medications (for example, control of medications, inspection of storage areas, removal of medications) not available.
[4] How do you detect diversion?		✓	Procedures needed to keep medications secure. Procedures for inspecting medication storage areas are not being followed.	

(continued)

Interview Subject: Nurse Manager (continued)

Questions	Correct Answer	Incorrect Answer	Follow-Up Needed	Comments or Notes
[5] What education do patients receive when being provided with sample medications? Are written instructions provided?	✓			
[6] What is the process for collecting medication information from the patients? Who is responsible for collecting the information?	✓			
[7] Is this information compiled and reconciled at each visit? What department is responsible for reconciling the information?		✓	Collect and analyze data about medication reconciliation to determine effectiveness of processes.	Nurse did not clearly understand her responsibilities and the organization's medication reconciliation tool. Process was not standardized.
[8] Are patients encouraged to maintain a medication profile and to bring it to each clinic visit?	✓			

Interview Subject: Patients

Questions	Correct Answer	Incorrect Answer	Follow-Up Needed	Comments or Notes
[9] Do you maintain a list of all the medications you are taking? Explain why you think having this list is a good idea.	✓			
[10] Do you bring the list with you to all clinic visits?	✓			
[11] Have you received education regarding the proper use of your medications?	✓			

Interview Subject: *Frontline Nurse*				
Questions	**Correct Answer**	**Incorrect Answer**	**Follow-Up Needed**	**Comments or Notes**
[12] What issues have been identified regarding control, labeling, security, and documentation of sample medications?	✓			
[13] Has patient access to sample medications been identified as a safety risk, and if so, what has been done to minimize this risk?		✓	*Need incentives or other program to establish mindfulness and habit for securing sample medications.*	*Nurse admitted lack of consistent attention to medication security.*
[14] What improvements have been implemented to correct any problems related to management of sample medications?		✓	*Need leadership to take a role in making security of sample medications a priority.*	
[15] Explain the process used to obtain accurate and complete medication histories from patients. How do you know that this process is being carried out?	✓			

Tracer Scenarios for
BEHAVIORAL HEALTH CARE

NOTE: No Two Tracers Are the Same

Please keep in mind that each tracer is unique. There is no way to know all of the questions that might be asked or documents that might be reviewed during a tracer—or what all the responses to the questions and documents might be. The possibilities are limitless, depending on the tracer topic and the organization's circumstances. These tracer scenarios and sample questions are provided as educational or training tools for organization staff; they are not scripts for real or mock tracers.

Section Elements

This section includes sample tracers—called scenarios—relevant to behavioral health care. The section is organized as follows:

Scenarios: Each scenario presents what might happen when a surveyor conducts a specific type of tracer. The scenarios are presented in an engaging narrative format in which the reader "follows" the surveyor through the tracer scenario. Within the narrative are bracketed numbers that correspond to numbered sample tracer questions following the tracer.

Sample Tracer Questions: After each scenario narrative is a list of sample questions a surveyor might ask during that scenario. These questions can be used to develop and conduct mock tracers in your organization on topics similar to those covered in the scenario.

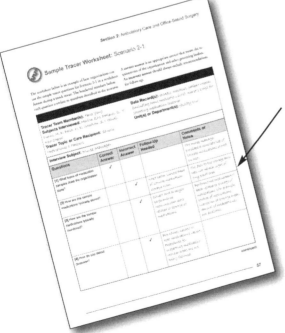

Sample Tracer Worksheet: At the end of the section is a sample worksheet that shows how the sample tracer questions for one select scenario in the section might be used in a worksheet format. The example shows how the worksheet might be completed as part of a tracer for that scenario. A blank form of the worksheet is available in Appendix B.

SCENARIO 3-1. Community Mental Health Center

Summary

In the following scenario, a surveyor conducted a medication management tracer at a community mental health center. Within the tracer, the surveyor explored issues relating to these priority focus areas:

- Medication Management
- Organization Structure
- Information Management
- Quality Improvement Expertise/Activities

Scenario

The surveyor conducted this medication management tracer in a community mental health center that provided medication services in an array of settings. These included a 24-hour crisis stabilization unit (CSU), a residential setting, an Assertive Community Treatment (ACT) program, and outpatient medication management. The focus of this tracer was medication management in the treatment program and outpatient treatment.

(Bracketed numbers correlate to Sample Tracer Questions on pages 64–65.)

➜ *Exploring Strategies with the Performance Improvement Committee.* The surveyor met with the performance improvement (PI) committee, which included the PI director and clinical and PI leaders at the organization. [1–2] The surveyor asked who was responsible for coordinating or overseeing implementation and/or finding the best-practice procedures used in the center's various programs. [3] The group explained that medication management practices differed by program and that the organization did not have a single person who was responsible for medication management systemwide. The senior nursing staff member or a single nursing staff member from each program was responsible for his or her program and thus for any medication management procedures that were introduced in that individual program. For example, there was one nurse assigned to the ACT program, and he designed the medication management practices for that particular program. [4] The committee was not sure if any of these program managers collected or analyzed any kind of data regarding their program's medication processes. [5]

➜ *Touring Storage Areas with the PI Director.* Following the discussion with the PI committee, the surveyor asked the PI director to show her where sample medications for the entire organization were stored. The director explained that there was no single storage area. Medications used by a particular program were stored in that program's staff office area, separated from medications used in the other outpatient programs. As they visited each of these storage areas, the surveyor noted that each program carefully identified medications, expiration dates, and lot numbers. The boxed samples in every area displayed expiration dates—written in bold, black permanent marker—on the outsides of the boxes. The samples with the closest expiration dates were stored in the front of the boxes, and those with the most distant dates in the rear of the boxes. [6] The surveyor asked staff in each program how that program tracked usage of its samples. [7] In each case, the surveyor was told that no tracking was done at all. Program staff said the samples were given out to patients by physicians until they simply ran out and more were ordered.

➜ *Visiting with ACT Personnel.* The surveyor next visited with the ACT program's nurse manager. The nurse told the surveyor that there were no stock medications. Medication (other than samples) to be taken to individuals served in the community were obtained by prescription from a local pharmacy. [8] These medications were stored in a small closet in the staff office area accessible by only a few ACT program staff members. The facility's general director was the only non–ACT person with access. [9]

Typically, the nurse manager explained, ACT nursing staff set out daily, weekly, and/or bi-weekly pill containers of medications for individuals served—sometimes in the program office and sometimes during home visits, depending on the individual's preferences and capabilities. At the surveyor's request, the manager stopped a nurse preparing to make a round of home visits. The surveyor asked to see her carrier, noting that it contained the appropriate supply of medication for each individual she was scheduled to visit. The carrier also contained gloves, a bottle of hand sanitizer, and, in the event that she had to give an injection, syringes, needles, and, a small sharps container for needle disposal. [10] She also had frozen packs to keep the medications she carried cool while in transit. [11] The nurse showed the surveyor that the carrier had a lock on it and stated that she kept it in the locked trunk of her car between visits. [12]

➜ *Observations at a Foster Care Home.* Later, accompanying another ACT nurse on a visit to the home of an 11-year-old male in therapeutic foster care, the surveyor discussed medication management practices with the foster parent. [13] The parent kept the youth's medications in a locked metal box. She also had a sheet that resembled a medication administration record (MAR) on which she and the youth documented when medications were taken. [14–15] The surveyor noted that all medications in the locked box were appropriately labeled and had distant expiration dates.

➡ *Back at the Center with the Psychiatrist.* After returning to the mental health center, the surveyor met with the staff psychiatrist and was able to review the foster child's clinical record. She noted that the youth was on several medications in the same psychotropic medication class. The surveyor then reviewed the organization's policy and procedure for this class of drugs. She found that guidelines for prescribing multiple psychotropic medications in the same class were quite clear and complete, requiring written justification for any deviation from guidelines. [16] Returning to the foster child's clinical record, the surveyor noticed that the physician notes did not include this justification. The psychiatrist, who was the only medical staff person who worked with children, told the surveyor that monitoring responses to medication was done primarily by medical staff and was based on reports to physicians and nurses about the individuals served. [17–19] He also said that the evaluation focused primarily on medication errors, which had steadily remained low in frequency for several years. [20]

➡ *Moving Forward.* Based on the tracer, the surveyor may discuss the following in the Daily Briefing: the need for better coordination and oversight of medication management across programs, especially in tracking samples and monitoring; identifying and implementing best, efficient, and safe practices for managing medications systemwide; improvements in staff documentation.

Scenario 3-1.
Sample Tracer Questions

The bracketed numbers before each question correlate to questions, observations, and data review described in the sample tracer for Scenario 3-1. You can use the tracer worksheet form in Appendix B to develop a mock tracer (*see* an example of a completed tracer worksheet at the end of this section). The information gained by conducting a mock tracer can help to highlight a good practice and/or determine issues that may require further follow-up.

PI Committee:

[1] Describe the medication system for your organization's various programs. How are medication management policies set and evaluated for each program?

[2] What does your organization look at in an evaluation of its medication management practices? How is the evaluation documented?

[3] Is there are an individual responsible for medication management systemwide?

[4] How is competency assessed for the nurses responsible for medication management in their specific programs?

[5] What types of data are tracked regarding the effectiveness of medication management processes?

PI Director:

[6] How are sample medications stored? How are these medications organized? Is the procedure the same for each program?

[7] How is usage of the sample medications tracked? Is this procedure the same for each program?

ACT Program Nurses:

[8] How do you obtain medications for individuals served?

[9] How are prescription medications secured in the program office? Who among staff has access to them?

[10] When off site, how do nurses practice hand hygiene and infection control?

[11] When off site, how do nurses ensure that medications being transported are stored at proper temperatures?

[12] How are transported medications secured?

Foster Parent and Youth:

[13] What kind of medications are currently being taken? What are they for? What are their side effects?

[14] What kind of education has the center provided regarding the medications? Have you been informed about the importance of keeping them secure? Have you been told to keep a record of all medication taken?

[15] Do you have any concerns about the medications?

Psychiatrist:

[16] What is the process for prescribing medications for an individual?

[17] How is the individual monitored regarding these medications over time?

[18] How are the side effects and responses to medications taken (for example, weight gain, metabolic syndrome, loss of libido) documented and used?

[19] What is the protocol for changing an individual's medication? How are changes to medication communicated to other staff members?

[20] How are medication errors reported, documented, and used to improve processes?

SCENARIO 3-2. Day Treatment Program

Summary

In the following scenario, a surveyor conducted a medication management tracer at a day treatment program. Within the tracer, the surveyor explored issues relating to these priority focus areas:
- Medication Management
- Quality Improvement Expertise/Activities
- Communication
- Patient Safety

Scenario

The surveyor conducted a medication management tracer in a partial hospitalization program for adults with behavioral diagnoses in which individuals served step down to less intensive outpatient programming as their conditions improve. Programming ran for approximately three hours each day, with one group served in the mornings and one in the afternoons. The program worked with a single psychiatrist whose services were contracted.

(Bracketed numbers correlate to Sample Tracer Questions on page 66.)

➡ *Discussing Prescribing and Monitoring.* In an interview with the program director, the surveyor learned that medications were not administered at the facility. Rather, individuals served live at home or in group homes, with their medications stored and received at those locations. [1] Because of this arrangement, the program director explained, the organization did not address the issue of adverse medication reactions. [2] Further, the organization had not implemented any kind of evaluation of its medication management program, as it operated

under the thought that, again, such a requirement applied only to organizations that stored or administered medication. [3]

The program director explained that individuals served were able to see the program's psychiatrist on site for management of psychotropic medications. [4] The surveyor asked to see the organization's written policies and procedures addressing the use of multiple psychotropic agents in the same class, the use of high-dose pharmacotherapy, and the identification and management of side effects such as tardive dyskinesia. [5] He also asked to see documentation of any observations following the use of prescribed medications. [6] The program director said that the organization simply had no written policies and procedures or documentation regarding the use of medications because, again, those issues were left to the discretion of the psychiatrist. [7]

➡ *Interviewing the Psychiatrist.* Following the report from the program director, the surveyor had a telephone discussion with the psychiatrist, who was not scheduled to be on site at the time of the tracer. The psychiatrist explained that she had her own protocol that she used in determining whether and when to use multiple psychotropic medications in the same class. [8] She stated that she never used high-dose pharmacotherapy and that she did her own Abnormal Involuntary Movement Scale (AIMS) testing quarterly on individuals on prescribed medications that put them at risk for tardive dyskinesia. She said that she discussed possible side effects with individuals served when she started them on a medication, and she asked if they were experiencing any side effects each time she saw them, [9] adding that if they reported side effects she responded accordingly.

➡ *With an Individual Served.* The surveyor next talked with one of the individuals served who was receiving antipsychotic medications. This person shared generally positive responses about the program, the accessibility of the pychiatrist and staff, and the improvements in his life as a result of attending the program. [10–11] He told the surveyor that the psychiatrist informed him about the possible side effects of medication, including weight gain. He did not like this particular side effect, but he did not seem to think there was much that could be done about it. The man told the surveyor that he had not complained about weight gain to the psychiatrist but had discussed the issue with his counselor. [12]

➡ *Moving Forward.* Based on the tracer, the surveyor may discuss the following in the Daily Briefing: the lack of attention to adverse medication reactions and evaluation of the medication management system and the risks this represents; the possible need for more involvement in the program and more interaction with individuals served by the psychiatrist.

Scenario 3-2.
Sample Tracer Questions

The bracketed numbers before each question correlate to questions, observations, and data review described in the sample tracer for Scenario 3-2. You can use the tracer worksheet form in Appendix B to develop a mock tracer (*see* an example of a completed tracer worksheet at the end of this section). The information gained by conducting a mock tracer can help to highlight a good practice and/or determine issues that may require further follow-up.

Program Director:

[1]   What are the program's policies and procedures for medication management?

[2]   How do you monitor adverse medication reactions?

[3]   Explain the evaluation process for the medication management program.

[4]   How are psychotropic medications managed?

[5]   Does the organization know the specific protocols for decision making regarding the use of multiple psychotropic medications in the same class?

[6]   What is the process for sharing observations about the effects of medications on individuals served?

[7]   Does the organization monitor the psychiatrist's prescribing practices against these protocols?

Psychiatrist:

[8]   Explain the protocols you use to prescribe multiple psychotropic medications.

[9]   How do you communicate with individuals served about possible side effects of medications?

Individual Served:

[10]   Describe your experiences in the day treatment program.

[11]   Is the program meeting your needs?

[12]   What do you do if you are dissatisfied with the side effects caused by your medications? To whom do you speak?

SCENARIO 3-3. Residential Program

Summary

In the following scenario, a surveyor conducted a medication management tracer at a residential program. Within the tracer, the surveyor explored issues relating to these priority focus areas:

- Medication Management
- Communication
- Orientation & Training
- Quality Improvement Expertise/Activities

Scenario

The surveyor conducted a medication management tracer in a residential treatment program for individuals with co-occurring mental illness and substance abuse issues. The parent organization had two such sites along with an outpatient setting, all at different locations.

(Bracketed numbers correlate to Sample Tracer Questions on pages 67–68.)

➡ *Meeting with Leadership.* The surveyor first talked with the program director and the parent organization's nursing director about the medications prescribed for residents. The surveyor learned that these medications were obtained from a local community pharmacy and were stored and controlled. The organization was responsible for monitoring responses to the medications. [1] Self-administration of medications occurred under the observation of trained, nonlicensed, nonmedical personnel. [2–3]

The program director told the surveyor that the organization relied on two family practice physicians, both under contract, to conduct physical health screenings and physical examinations. A psychiatrist, under contract for psychiatric services, prescribed and monitored responses to psychotropic medications.

➡ *Talking with a Member of Staff.* The surveyor next met with one of the organization's nonmedical, nonlicensed staff members responsible for monitoring the distribution of medication. [4] He explained that he and others employed in the same role spent three weeks of intense training and mentoring before being assigned a regular shift on the floor. [5]

He told the surveyor that medications were stored in a small office off the main staff station near the living room as he showed the surveyor the medications stored by users' names. [6] He mentioned that over-the-counter medications were also obtained and stored for each person, though not in stock quantities.

The organization had specific times when medications were distributed, so the surveyor was able to observe the distribution and self-administration process. [7] Staff members working in pairs distributed assigned medication containers along with a cup containing either water or juice. Residents self-administered their medications, then initialed a medication administration record (MAR) for the date and time. One of the two staff members also initialed that the appropriate medication had been taken by the correct person. [8]

After all medication was distributed, the staff member responded to the surveyor's additional questions, informing him that medications were prescribed by the physicians. [9] These prescribers were also responsible for informing residents about the benefits and risks of medications they prescribed. [10] Staff members faxed the prescriptions to a retail pharmacy, which delivered them the same day. Policies and procedures detailed what should be done if new medications were needed between physician visits. [11–12]

➡ *Discussing Medication Management and Errors.* Joined once again by the parent organization's nursing director, the surveyor reviewed documentation regarding medication errors that had been reported over the previous three months. [13–14] The surveyor learned that the organization's self-evaluation of its medication management process focused only on reports of medication errors—and there were very few of them. The organization did not regularly evaluate data over time or look for improvement activities in the associated processes. It did no evaluation of medication use or effectiveness patterns. Further, it did not use a recent medication error to generate any kind of performance improvement for its training, ordering, or prescribing processes. [15–17]

➡ *Moving Forward.* Based on the tracer, the surveyor may discuss the following in the Daily Briefing: a review of policies and procedures regarding medication orders; including more detail in training curriculum documentation to establish how nonmedical staff are trained; establishing a more comprehensive approach to error identification, analysis, and action.

Scenario 3-3.
Sample Tracer Questions

The bracketed numbers before each question correlate to questions, observations, and data review described in the sample tracer for Scenario 3-3. You can use the tracer worksheet form in Appendix B to develop a mock tracer (*see* an example of a completed tracer worksheet at the end of this section). The information gained by conducting a mock tracer can help to highlight a good practice and/or determine issues that may require further follow-up.

Program Director and Nursing Director:
[1] Describe how the residents' responses are monitored. Who handles this?

[2] How do you determine and ensure required competencies for your staff?

[3] How do you determine qualifications for contract staff?

Nonmedical Staff Person:
[4] What is your role as a nonmedical, nonlicensed staff member?

[5] What training have you received regarding medication management?

[6] Can you show me how and where medications are stored?

[7] Describe the process of distributing medications and your exact role in it.

[8] How do you identify individuals served before dispensing medications to them?

[9] What is the process for ordering prescriptions?

[10] Who is responsible for asking residents about the impact of new medications? How is this information documented?

[11] What do you do if an individual served needs new medications between physician visits?

[12] What do you do if you have questions regarding a medication order for an individual served?

Nursing Director:
[13] Are near misses tracked? If so, how is information about near misses used to improve performance?

[14] What process is used to discover the underlying causes of medication errors? How is the information used to improve performance?

(continued)

Scenario 3-3.
Sample Tracer Questions (continued)

[15] How do you determine and ensure required competencies for staff?

[16] Are data on errors used to guide training for staff?

[17] How do you use data to improve order-writing policies and procedures?

SCENARIO 3-4. Child/Youth Addiction Services Program

Summary

In the following scenario, a surveyor conducted a medication management tracer in a child/youth addiction services program. Within the tracer, the surveyor explored issues relating to these priority focus areas:

- Medication Management
- Patient Safety
- Communication
- Assessment and Care/Services
- Quality Improvement Expertise/Activities

Scenario

The surveyor was in the process of finishing a tracer in a residential child/youth addiction services program. She had specifically focused the tracer on the monitoring of medications and was now in the final phases of the tracer—the last stop in a tour of the facility, to be followed by a wrap-up session with staff.

(Bracketed numbers correlate to Sample Tracer Questions at right and pages 69.)

➔ *Visiting the Medication Room.* The final stop of the tour in progress was the medication room, where the surveyor asked a nurse what high-alert medications are identified as particular concerns. [1–2] The nurse said that none of the medications in use in the program were considered high alert, but that the organization did have a list of look-alike/sound-alike medications. [3] She removed it from a nearby procedures manual for the surveyor to review. [4] She explained that each nurse prevented errors by being extra careful in checking this list as well as checking the medication he or she administered against the medication administration record (MAR). [5] The

nurse also said that physicians wrote orders for medications such as divalproex sodium and carbamazepine. Physicians then monitored residents on such medications for weight gain and suicidal ideation. [6]

➔ *Meeting with the Team.* Finally, the surveyor met in a conference room with staff members and counselors to conclude the tracer with a discussion of the medications amphetamine and dextroamphetamine, the prescribing and administering of which had come up multiple times in the preceding tracer. She was told by the staff members and counselors present that weekly team meetings included a review of the target symptoms, which were specifically identified in the physician orders for each medication. [7–8] The teachers, counselors, and case management staff in the program completed daily tracking sheets on the target symptoms and used the sheets as the basis for evaluating the effectiveness of these medications on specific symptoms. [9–10]

Generally, in speaking with staff throughout the tracer, the surveyor had learned that they felt like a significant part of the team and that their input mattered regarding the management of all medications used in the program. [11] In addition, they noted that treatment planning was immediately responsive to any failure to improve. As a result, they felt that they were more effective in their jobs. Finally, the surveyor learned that the organization planned to begin collecting outcome data as part of PI activities. [12]

➔ *Moving Forward.* Based on the tracer, the surveyor may discuss the following in the Daily Briefing: institution of a regular brainstorming session on ways to prevent medication errors, such as the organization's multidisciplinary approach to monitoring amphetamine and dextroamphetamine use.

Scenario 3-4.
Sample Tracer Questions

The bracketed numbers before each question correlate to questions, observations, and data review described in the sample tracer for Scenario 3-4. You can use the tracer worksheet form in Appendix B to develop a mock tracer (*see* an example of a completed tracer worksheet at the end of this section). The information gained by conducting a mock tracer can help to highlight a good practice and/or determine issues that may require further follow-up.

Nursing Staff:

[1] How does the organization define high-alert medications?

[2] How are you involved in the medication management process?

[3] What practices are in place to prevent errors due to look-alike/sound-alike medications? How are staff members made aware of these selected medications?

[4] Have the use of look-alike/sound-alike medications been made a part of your policies and procedures?

[5] What types of training have you received related to the prevention of medication errors?

[6] How is competency assessed for staff who play a role in the medication management process?

Program Staff Members and Counselors:

[7] How does the organization seek to improve medication safety and reduce the risk of medication errors?

[8] What training have you had in observing and reporting on side effects and adverse reactions to medications?

[9] How do you report medication compliance?

[10] If you observe any unusual behavior, symptoms of physical illness, and/or side effects of medications, who do you notify? How do you make notification?

[11] What steps are taken to involve staff in decision making within the program? How has this contributed to staff morale?

[12] How are data used to improve performance related to medication management?

SCENARIO 3-5. Opioid Program

Summary

In the following scenario, a surveyor conducted a medication management tracer in an opioid treatment program. Within the tracer, the surveyor explored issues relating to these priority focus areas:

- Medication Management
- Patient Safety
- Quality Improvement Expertise/Activities

Scenario

This tracer was conducted at an opioid treatment program, where the clinic's program director was also the nursing director.

The surveyor met with her and one of the nurses who administered methadone and other medications to the individuals served.

(Bracketed numbers correlate to Sample Tracer Questions on pages 70–71.)

➡ *Interviewing the Program Director.* In a brief question and answer session with the program director, the surveyor began by asking the director to describe the clinic's medication management process and to explain how that process was monitored. [1–2] The director told her about the program's three-phase process involving treatment of physical withdrawal, treatment for cravings, and treatment to maintain abstinence. The program routinely used drugs like methadone, naltrexone, and buprenorphine during all three phases, but most often during the early stages of treatment, depending on the addiction and specific treatment plan. She emphasized staff adherence to the program's strict policies and procedures regarding medication diversion control, [3–4] storage, and safety, as well as management's focus on data collection, [5] patient education, and staff training. [6–8] She also explained that she set aside time during monthly staff training sessions to discuss safety issues, particularly medication safety concerns.

Recalling the director's repeated references throughout the day to severely limited funding, the surveyor asked if the clinic employed automated systems to track dosing and administration of the various medications used. [9–10] The director admitted that much discussion surrounding such systems had occurred, but nothing along these lines was in place yet. The surveyor asked how she stayed apprised of new developments in medication safety while dealing with limited financial resources. [11] The program director said that she regularly checked the major professional, state, and federal agencies for updates and was on various organizations' electronic mailing lists for medication safety updates.

➡ *Touring the Clinic with a Nurse.* After the discussion with the program director, the surveyor toured the clinic with a nurse. He showed the surveyor where methadone in particular was stored, described the processes for receiving it, and explained the administration process for it. [12] He added that very similar procedures were used for the other drugs used in the program. The nurse told the surveyor that he was one of only a few who had access to the storage area. Others with access included the medical director, program director, and two others of the nursing staff. [13]

The surveyor asked what kind of medication education was communicated to individuals served and how staff provided ongoing education to them. [14–15] The nurse detailed how this was done during initial assessment and continued during treatment. The program's medical director and nursing staff closely monitored medications and communicated safe practices to individuals served, as well.

The surveyor then asked about the take-home medication process and what types of safety measures and diversion control measures were in place. The nurse described the diversion control plan the clinic had in place. He added that staff diversion seemed to be "a big deal" at the clinic. As the nurse had mentioned, the surveyor noticed that purses, backpacks, and other personal items owned by staff were indeed kept in the dispensing station, which could present a diversion risk. [16–17]

As the tour ended, the surveyor had an opportunity to observe the administration process to see if actual practice matched some of what the nurse had been describing. [18–19] She saw that a nurse on duty administered medication properly and took appropriate measures to correctly identify the individual receiving medication by asking for two identifiers, as required in National Patient Safety Goal NPSG.01.01.01 (*see* Appendix E, page 151). [20]

➡ *Interviewing an Individual Served.* The surveyor interviewed an individual served about his experiences at the program. [21–23] He described various safety-related practices, including keeping his methadone in a locked container, stored on a closet shelf in his bedroom, to keep his children from getting to it. [24] He noted that staff had gone over safety practices and diversion-control practices in detail when he was first given take-home medication, and then again a couple weeks later. [25]

➡ *Moving Forward.* Based on the tracer, the surveyor may discuss the following in the Daily Briefing: the clinic's lack of a fully automated process for medication administration as a method of greatly reducing the risk of errors and actual errors; regular review of diversion-control practices within and particularly outside the clinic; including role-playing to assess how staff and individuals served respond to various potential diversion situations.

Scenario 3-5.
Sample Tracer Questions

The bracketed numbers before each question correlate to questions, observations, and data review described in the sample tracer for Scenario 3-5. You can use the tracer worksheet form in Appendix B to develop a mock tracer (*see* an example of a completed tracer worksheet at the end of this section). The information gained by conducting a mock tracer can help to highlight a good practice and/or determine issues that may require further follow-up.

Program Director:

[1] What is the medication management process for the opioid treatment program?

[2] How is the medication process monitored for the opioid treatment program?

[3] What procedures are used to minimize staff diversion risks?

[4] Who is responsible for diversion-control activities?

[5] What kind of medication-related data does your organization collect?

[6] What kind of education to individuals served do you provide about medication?

[7] How do you verify that the education is understood?

[8] How do you orient and train new staff on your medication management practices?

[9] What kind of automated systems do you use to track dosing and administration of medication?

[10] How have you trained staff on this process?

[11] How do you keep up to date on safe medication practices?

Nurse:

[12] Where does your organization store its methadone supply?

[13] Who has access to the methadone supply? Do you have access to it?

[14] How do you educate individuals served about medications in general?

[15] How are you involved in educating individuals served about methadone?

[16] What steps has your organization taken to reduce diversion?

[17] Who is responsible for diversion-control activities?

[18] Describe your medication administration process.

[19] How do you assess an individual served for medication safety?

[20] How do you identify individuals served before administering medications?

Individual Served:

[21] Describe your experience with your treatments here at the program.

[22] Do you think the program is meeting your needs?

[23] If you have a concern about your treatment, how do you report it?

[24] How did staff first educate you on the safe use of your medications? What steps do you take to keep your medication secure in your own home?

[25] How do staff offer follow-up education?

SCENARIO 3-6. Outdoor Wilderness Program

Summary

In the following scenario, a surveyor conducted a medication management tracer in an outdoor wilderness program. Within the tracer, the surveyor explored issues relating to these priority focus areas:

- Medication Management
- Patient Safety
- Quality Improvement Expertise/Activities

Scenario

This tracer was conducted at an outdoor wilderness program for teenagers with behavioral health issues. Prior to embarking on their outdoor experience, the adolescents participating received residential treatment services for at least one month, during which time they were evaluated for their ability to benefit from and participate in the outdoor portion of the program.

(Bracketed numbers correlate to Sample Tracer Questions on page 72.)

➡ *Discussing the Program with Leaders.* In discussing the program's structure and goals with organizational leaders, the surveyor focused his attention on primary medication management practices during the outdoor experience portion of the program. [1] He noted that this involved emergency preparedness, storage and transport, and self-administration of medication. [2] Nursing and medical staff did not regularly participate in the "outdoor" phase of the program. Thus, trained nonmedical staff, called counselors, oversaw medication needs while youth were participating in that phase. [3]

The organization purchased commercially prepared wilderness medical first-aid kits and maintained a restocking contract with the makers of the kit. [4] The counselors were all trained in cardiopulmonary resuscitation (CPR) and first aid, as well as in the use of the contents of the first-aid kits. A family practice physician reviewed the contents of the kit and added items that he thought would be important, including an epinephrine auto-injector. [5] The surveyor found that documentation of all medical incidents and incidents requiring first aid was complete.

➡ *Discussing the Program with Nonmedical Staff.* Later in the tracer, two of the counselors that accompany the adolescents on the wilderness trips continued the leader's description of the program. [6] Review trainings and debriefings specific to medical situations were held with the organization physician and nurse after each trip, they explained. [7] Incident reports were completed on any medication errors and were evaluated as part of the debriefing. [8] The counselors said that plans for procedural changes were also developed during and after the debriefing meetings. The surveyor asked counselors to describe examples of process changes resulting from a medication-related incident or unwanted occurrence. [9] The counselors were able to site quite a few.

➡ *A Conversation with Individuals Served.* At the encouragement of the program leader, the surveyor was also able to talk with two adolescents who had participated in several wilderness experiences. Each had experienced a minor medical emergency during a trip, requiring a counselor to use one of the first-aid kits and some of the medication within them. [10] They told the surveyor that despite the incidents, they were very happy with the experience and reported having had no significant or ongoing medical problems. [11]

➡ *Moving Forward.* Based on the tracer, the surveyor may discuss the following in the Daily Briefing: continued education on emergency preparedness for medications, particularly in outdoor settings; documentation of changes to the first-aid kits.

Scenario 3-6.
Sample Tracer Questions

The bracketed numbers before each question correlate to questions, observations, and data review described in the sample tracer for Scenario 3-6. You can use the tracer worksheet form in Appendix B to develop a mock tracer (*see* an example of a completed tracer worksheet at the end of this section). The information gained by conducting a mock tracer can help to highlight a good practice and/or determine issues that may require further follow-up.

Leaders:

[1]   How do you review the appropriateness of the medication management practices followed while clients are participating in program outings?

[2]   Please explain your program's medication management process.

[3]   What are the medication needs of your clients? How do you know this?

[4]   What type of medical equipment is used during the program outings? How is it selected? How is it maintained?

[5]   If nonmedical personnel are responsible for adolescents on these outings, how are trained medical staff involved in the process?

Nonmedical Staff:

[6]   What training have you received related to medication and the needs of clients during program activities?

[7]   How do you share medication-related experiences with the prescribing licensed independent practitioner?

[8]   How do you track medication errors? How do you use the resulting information to improve organization performance?

[9]   Are you involved in PI activities related to medication management? Please provide an example of your involvement.

Adolescents Served:

[10]   If you take medications, how do you take them when you are in the program?

[11]   If you have a concern, how do you share that concern?

SCENARIO 3-7. Community Mental Health Center

Summary

In the following scenario, a surveyor conducted a medication management system tracer in a community mental health center. Within the tracer, the surveyor explored issues relating to these priority focus areas:
- Medication Management
- Quality Improvement Expertise/Activities

Scenario

The surveyor conducted this tracer in a crisis stabilization unit (CSU) at a community mental health center. Medications were ordered for individuals by prescription from an off-site pharmacy. The CSU stored a limited supply of stock medications that were most frequently needed for emergency admissions to the CSU, as well as supplies of over-the-counter (OTC) medications. The surveyor visited two locations in the center as part of a short tour, and then talked with the center's director.

(Bracketed numbers correlate to Sample Tracer Questions on pages 73–74.)

➡ *In the Medication Room.* First visiting the medication room, the surveyor asked a nurse how look-alike/sound-alike medications were handled. [1] The nurse said there was a list of look-alike/sound-alike medications and proceeded to spend a lengthy amount of time searching for it. He eventually found it behind some other documents. The surveyor asked if the organization had implemented any practices to reduce errors associated with the medications on the list. [2] The nurse said the organization relied on "extra-careful checking procedures" when setting up medications for administration. He said he occasionally used some of the medications on the list with patients but was not aware of any additional error-/risk-reduction procedures other than the list itself. [3]

The surveyor then asked the nurse to pull the record of someone who had been receiving services from the CSU for some time. She asked the nurse to use it as an example to illustrate various steps in the center's medication process. The record presented was that of a 52-year-old woman who had been in and out of treatment at the center for the past 10 years and was currently on olanzapine, among other medications. The nurse walked the surveyor through the process of obtaining, ordering, and administering medications, as well as monitoring individuals who were starting on new medications. [4]

→ *In the Medication Preparation Area.* The second stop on the tour was in the medication preparation area, where a second nurse walked the surveyor through the setup of medications for administration, including the double-checking procedures. [5] The nurse's brief presentation included a description of appropriate procedures for using two patient identifiers before administering any medications. [6]

The surveyor then asked if the organization ever took telephone orders. [7] The nurse said that it did, and when he took a phone order, he wrote the information on a nearby scrap of paper, read it back to the physician ordering the medication, and then copied the approved order onto the order sheet in the clinical record. The surveyor asked if the nurse thought there was an additional risk of error in using this technique and explained that organization policy required the writing of an order on the order sheet and reading that back for accuracy verification. The nurse noted he was aware of the policy, but was just trying to keep from having to draw lines through anything in the chart.

The surveyor asked whether individuals served could bring in their own medications from outside of the organization for their use. [8] The nurse explained that this was acceptable if the medications could be verified and if the attending physician ordered them to be used. The nurse showed the surveyor the written policies and procedures that addressed this practice. According to these, any medications brought in by the individual served had to be in an appropriately labeled medication bottle, with its contents verified by the nursing staff through the use of an online program. The policy stated that the prescribing physician and/or dispensing pharmacist must be contacted for further verification that the medication was prescribed for that individual served. All verification procedures were documented in the clinical record. Orders given by the attending physician were written for the specific medication, dose, and frequency. The organization did not allow self-administration of medication on this CSU unit.

→ *Meeting with the Center Director.* After the tour and in a meeting with the center director, the surveyor learned that physicians were responsible for explaining the benefits, risks, and side effects of new medications to individuals served. [9] All individuals served received a simplified description of these items in writing as part of that process. Upon administering medications, nurses reinforced this information and instructed the individuals served to check back with them if they experienced any side effects or adverse reactions. The director stated that nurses routinely checked with individuals served about how they were feeling, but there was neither a systematic way of prompting for

this nor indicating that it happened. [10–11] Nursing notes and counselor notes on the 52-year-old woman being traced did not contain any observations evaluating the impact of medication on the individual's presentation of symptoms, although the nurse could describe verbally what symptom changes had occurred Within the tracer individual's stay at the CSU.

→ *Moving Forward.* Based on the tracer, the surveyor may discuss the following in the Daily Briefing: CSU development of look-alike/sound-alike medication risk reduction strategies (such as storing these medications in separate bins or placing alert stickers on the medications); confirmation of telephone orders through a read-back process.

Scenario 3-7.
Sample Tracer Questions

The bracketed numbers before each question correlate to questions, observations, and data review described in the sample tracer for Scenario 3-7. You can use the tracer worksheet form in Appendix B to develop a mock tracer (*see* an example of a completed tracer worksheet at the end of this section). The information gained by conducting a mock tracer can help to highlight a good practice and/or determine issues that may require further follow-up.

Medication Room Nurse:

[1] What policies, procedures, or practices are used for look-alike/sound-alike medications?

[2] How are look-alike/sound-alike medications stored? What precautions are in place to prevent errors when look-alike/sound-alike meds are ordered?

[3] What training and orientation have you received specific to medication management? How is competency assessed?

[4] How do you monitor individuals starting on new medications?

Medication Preparation Area Nurse:

[5] What policies, procedures, or practices are used for the administration of medications?

[6] How do you ensure that the correct individual is receiving the correct medication?

[7] Are telephone orders permitted? If so, please explain your process for receiving such orders.

[8] How are medications that individuals bring into the CSU tracked, stored, and monitored?

(continued)

Scenario 3-7.
Sample Tracer Questions (continued)

[9] How are reactions to medications monitored? As standard practice, do you ask individuals served what side effects to watch for?

[10] What policies and procedures exist for monitoring of the effects of medications on individuals served in the CSU?

[11] What policies and procedures are used to determine how nurses are qualified to participate in medication management processes?

SCENARIO 3-8. Group Home

Summary

In the following scenario, a surveyor conducted a medication management system tracer in a group home. Within the tracer, the surveyor explored issues relating to these priority focus areas:

- Medication Management
- Communication
- Quality Improvement Expertise/Activities

Scenario

The surveyor conducted a medication management tracer in a group home for adult veterans who presented a range of psychiatric problems, especially posttraumatic stress disorder (PTSD).

(Bracketed numbers correlate to Sample Tracer Questions on page 75.)

➡ *Meeting with Leaders.* The parent organization with which this group home was associated provided a variety of treatment services at its other sites. The surveyor attended a meeting that included the specific group home manager for this site, as well as the larger organization's program and nursing directors. The nursing director explained that she made quarterly visits to each group home in the organization that required nursing staff onsite to inspect its medication management processes.

In this particular home, medications were prescribed by an internist and a psychiatrist whose medication management services were contracted. [1–2] The organization also had a

contractual arrangement with a local community pharmacy for obtaining medications and for verifying any that might be brought in by the individual served at the time of admission. The surveyor was told that medications were controlled and self-administered by residents.

The surveyor asked the program manager how she identified medication errors and what she thought the most frequently occurring error was. The program manager said that errors were tracked from medication administration record (MAR) sheets. [3] She noted that the most frequent problem was missed medications and that it was an issue that was currently being addressed. She said a meeting with staff and current residents was being planned to identify ways to help residents remember to take their medications. At previous meetings about this problem, staff and residents had reported that the causes for missed medications were forgetting, doing something else when the medication was due, and sleeping through a medication time. [4]

➡ *With an Admissions Staff Member.* Building on the idea that medication use is a shared responsibility, the surveyor next visited with a member of the group home's admissions staff, asking about efforts to teach good medication management practices to individuals served. [5–6] The surveyor asked a staff member what processes guided self-administration of medications. [7–8] The staff member said nonmedical staff receive training on these processes at hire and periodically thereafter. [9]

The staff member reported that the organization had developed a procedure where a small section of each resident's personal clothes cabinet was equipped with a lock. Residents were to keep their medications in those secured sections of the cabinets in their rooms. Each resident wrote out his or her own MAR with the help of trained staff at admission and updated it whenever their medications were changed. [10] The resident kept this documentation, along with any information on benefits and side effects, in the cabinet as well. Each time a resident took his or her medications, the resident initialed the MAR in the correct location. Evening staff reviewed MAR documentation with residents on a daily basis for the first month of their stay and then weekly thereafter. The staff member was unable to explain how the documentation data was used to improve medication management processes. [11–12]

➡ *Talking with a Resident.* The surveyor also met with one of the residents of the group home and discussed his history, why he was living in the group home, and what medications he was taking. [13] The resident showed the surveyor his area and explained the entire medication process—obtaining, storing, taking, and tracking the medications. He showed the surveyor his locked clothes cabinet where he kept his medications along with the MAR. The resident said he understood the importance of completing the MAR, although he said he had occasionally missed medications because he had forgotten to take them. He was also able to describe the target symptoms for which he took medications as well as the most common side effects of his medications. [14–15]

➡ *Moving Forward.* Based on the tracer, the surveyor may discuss the following in the Daily Briefing: development of strategies to ensure residents take all prescribed medications on a timely basis; improving the medication management processes based on collected data.

Scenario 3-8.
Sample Tracer Questions

The bracketed numbers before each question correlate to questions, observations, and data review described in the sample tracer for Scenario 3-8. You can use the tracer worksheet form in Appendix B to develop a mock tracer (*see* an example of a completed tracer worksheet at the end of this section). The information gained by conducting a mock tracer can help to highlight a good practice and/or determine issues that may require further follow-up.

Organization Leaders:

[1]   Describe the group home's medication management process.

[2]   How are qualifications determined for contract staff?

[3]   How are medication errors tracked?

[4]   How are data about medication errors used to improve performance?

Admissions Staff Member:

[5]   Describe the medication management process and your role in that process.

[6]   How do you educate the residents about the medications they take?

[7]   Describe the policies and procedures that guide the self-administration of medications.

[8]   How is residents' self-administration of medications supervised?

[9]   What training have you received related to observing residents' self-administration of medications?

[10] Please explain your organization's documentation of medication management processes.

[11] How are data about medication errors used to improve performance?

[12] What is your role in improving processes related to medication management? Please describe an example of an improvement process.

Resident:

[13] What kinds of medications are you currently taking? What are they for? What are their side effects? Do you have any concerns about your medications?

[14] Describe any problems you have discovered with the self-administration program and how you have addressed them.

[15] What kind of education have you received about your medications?

Sample Tracer Worksheet: Scenario 3-1.

The worksheet below is an example of how organizations can use the sample tracer questions for Scenario 3-1 in a worksheet format during a mock tracer. The bracketed numbers before each question correlate to questions described in the scenario.

A **correct answer** is an appropriate answer that meets the requirements of the organization and other governing bodies. An **incorrect answer** should always include recommendations for follow-up.

Tracer Team Member(s): Melvin Savoy
Subjects Interviewed: Danielle Kapo, George Valente, Jason Strump, Kera Evanston, Nick Cabacas, Tina Fenton, Georgia Pacek, Anton Hudson, Laurence O'Dell
Tracer Topic or Care Recipient: Medication management in a community health care center with multiple programs; Anton Hudson

Data Record(s): Foster care parent's medication record; policies and procedures on psychotropic drugs, foster child's clinical record
Unit(s) or Department(s): ACT program area; foster care parent home

Interview Subject: PI Committee

Questions	Correct Answer	Incorrect Answer	Follow-Up Needed	Comments or Notes
[1] Describe the medication system for your organization's various programs. How are medication management policies set and evaluated for each program?	✓			
[2] What does your organization look at in an evaluation of its medication management practices? How is the evaluation documented?	✓			
[3] Is there are an individual responsible for medication management systemwide?		✓	Consider appointing systemwide person.	No one responsible systemwide, per policy.
[4] How is competency assessed for the nurses responsible for medication management in their specific programs?	✓			

Interview Subject: PI Committee (continued)

Questions	Correct Answer	Incorrect Answer	Follow-Up Needed	Comments or Notes
[5] What types of data are tracked regarding the effectiveness of medication management processes?		✓	Committee needs to address data collection and management regarding medication management processes—both within departments and systemwide.	Committee unaware of data on any particular program's medication management processes.

Interview Subject: PI Director

Questions	Correct Answer	Incorrect Answer	Follow-Up Needed	Comments or Notes
[6] How are sample medications stored? How are these medications organized? Is the procedure the same for each program?	✓			
[7] How is usage of the sample medications tracked? Is this procedure the same for each program?		✓	Need systemwide tracking policy and procedure for sample medications.	No tracking of sample medications; staff use products until out and order more.

Interview Subject: ACT Program Nurses

Question	Correct Answer	Incorrect Answer	Follow-Up Needed	Comments or Notes
[8] How do you obtain medications for individuals served?	✓			
[9] How are prescription medications secured in the program office? Who among staff has access to them?	✓			
[10] When off site, how do nurses practice hand hygiene and infection control?	✓			

(continued)

Interview Subject: ACT Program Nurses (continued)

Questions	Correct Answer	Incorrect Answer	Follow-Up Needed	Comments or Notes
[11] When off site, how do nurses ensure that medications being transported are stored at proper temperatures?	✓			
[12] How are transported medications secured?	✓			

Interview Subject: Foster Parent and Youth

Questions	Correct Answer	Incorrect Answer	Follow-Up Needed	Comments or Notes
[13] What kind of medications are currently being taken? What are they for? What are their side effects?		✓	May want to do further training on medication management for foster parents.	The foster parent was unable to remember any potential side effects of the medications and did not have educational materials on hand to refer to.
[14] What kind of education has the center provided regarding the medications? Have you been informed about the importance of keeping them secure? Have you been told to keep a record of all medication taken?	✓			
[15] Do you have any concerns about the medications?	✓			

Interview Subject: Psychiatrist

Questions	Correct Answer	Incorrect Answer	Follow-Up Needed	Comments or Notes
[16] What is the process for prescribing medications for an individual?	✓			

Interview Subject: Psychiatrist (continued)				
Questions	**Correct Answer**	**Incorrect Answer**	**Follow-Up Needed**	**Comments or Notes**
[17] How is the individual monitored regarding these medications over time?		✓	May need evaluation of coordination between policy and practice regarding monitoring.	Policy and practice were somewhat at odds regarding monitoring and any consequent deviations from guidelines.
[18] How are the side effects and responses to medications taken (for example, weight gain, metabolic syndrome, loss of libido) documented and used?	✓			
[19] What is the protocol for changing an individual's medication? How are changes to medication communicated to other staff members?		✓	See above note on monitoring.	See above note on monitoring.
[20] How are medication errors reported, documented, and used to improve processes?		✓	Incorporate data on medication errors into policy and procedure in a formal way rather than ad hoc.	No formal policy on how data on medication errors should affect policy on medication management.

Tracer Scenarios for
HOME CARE

NOTE: No Two Tracers Are the Same

Please keep in mind that each tracer is unique. There is no way to know all of the questions that might be asked or documents that might be reviewed during a tracer—or what all the responses to the questions and documents might be. The possibilities are limitless, depending on the tracer topic and the organization's circumstances. These tracer scenarios and sample questions are provided as educational or training tools for organization staff; they are not scripts for real or mock tracers.

Section Elements

This section includes sample tracers—called scenarios—relevant to home care. The section is organized as follows:

Scenarios: Each scenario presents what might happen when a surveyor conducts a specific type of tracer. The scenarios are presented in an engaging narrative format in which the reader "follows" the surveyor through the tracer scenario. Within the narrative are bracketed numbers that correspond to numbered sample tracer questions following the tracer.

Sample Tracer Questions: After each scenario narrative is a list of sample questions a surveyor might ask during that scenario. These questions can be used to develop and conduct mock tracers in your organization on topics similar to those covered in the scenario.

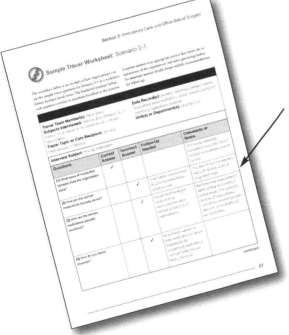

Sample Tracer Worksheet: At the end of the section is a sample worksheet that shows how the sample tracer questions for one select scenario in the section might be used in a worksheet format. The example shows how the worksheet might be completed as part of a tracer for that scenario. A blank form of the worksheet is available in Appendix B.

SCENARIO 4-1. Home Infusion Pharmacy Organization

Summary

In the following scenario, a surveyor conducted a medication management system tracer at a freestanding home infusion pharmacy organization. Within the tracer, the surveyor explored issues relating to these priority focus areas:

- Medication Management
- Information Management
- Patient Safety
- Quality Improvement Expertise/Activities

Scenario

Before accompanying a nurse on a home visit, the surveyor reviewed the organization's medication storage and administration policies to familarize himself with the organization's medication management process and to confirm that staff were caring for patients according to established policies, procedures, and protocols. He planned to observe patient care, conduct a brief interview with the patient, and return to the facility. Once up to speed, he and the nurse departed.

(Bracketed numbers correlate to Sample Tracer Questions on page 84.)

→ *In the Nurse's Car.* While driving to the patient's home, the surveyor asked the nurse to share her professional background and competencies. He then asked the nurse about the purpose of the visit, learning about the patient's condition and the care provided to date. Finally, the surveyor asked where the nurse stored medications for the patients she visited. The nurse explained that she always kept the medications she was transporting locked in the trunk of her car to secure them out of sight. [1] A short time later, the surveyor had the opportunity to see which medications she stored there. He found many of them not labeled with a patient's name. The surveyor and nurse discussed if it was legal for her to possess the medications, including an anaphylactic kit, without patient-specific labels attached to them. He knew that in some states nurses were not allowed to possess unlabeled prescription medications. [2]

The surveyor and the nurse discussed the possible effects on medications stored in a car trunk. As the surveyor pointed out, trunks could become quite hot in summer and very cold in the winter in that part of the country. [3] The nurse said that she did not know if it was safe to transport patients' medications

in her car trunk or if she could legally possess the medications without specific patients' names on their containers.

→ *Observing Patient Care.* The surveyor accompanied the nurse into the patient's home and observed how the nurse administered medication, changed dressings, drew blood, and provided education. He reviewed the nurse's notes section of the home care record and saw that this patient had been given sulfamethoxazole and trimethoprim intravenous (IV) therapy two weeks earlier, despite a notation in the patient's medication record that the patient was allergic to sulfonamides.

The patient, who among other issues was being treated for a urinary tract infection, explained that, as a rule, he avoided medications that contained ingredients with a "sul" or "sulfa" prefix. He said that he was aware that "some kinds of sulfur drugs" could trigger unpleasant allergy symptoms, some of which matched those he had noticed. [4] He did not remember anything in the information provided by the nurse or pharmacy that would have alerted him that the IV medication he received as part of treatment two weeks earlier did in fact contain sulfonamides. [5–6] On the way back to the agency, the surveyor talked with the nurse about how a patient with an allergy to sulfa could receive a medication in this drug class. [7]

→ *Telephoning the Contracted Pharmacy.* Back at the agency, the surveyor made an effort to determine if the organization's method of sharing allergy information with the nursing staff and the pharmacy were effective. He started by contacting the pharmacy utilized by the home health agency and had the opportunity to speak briefly via telephone with the pharmacist. They discussed the patient that suffered the adverse drug reaction (ADR) and how medications were received and dispensed by the pharmacy. [8–9] The pharmacist explained that drug allergy information was routinely entered into every patient's profile. He said that in case of that patient, however, it appeared that his information was somehow not obtained before the medication was dispensed. [10–11]

→ *Meeting with the Nursing Administrator.* The surveyor also shared his findings regarding the nurse's possession of unlabeled medication and its storage and transportation in the trunk of her car with the organization's nursing administrator. [12] She said that there was no state-level statute she was aware of regarding unlabeled drugs and that the organization was aware of the nurse's method of transporting medications to patients' homes. [13] There was no policy regarding this, and it was done routinely by all of the organization's nurses. [14]

Regarding the issue of the sulfa-allergic patient, the nurse administrator understood the issues, but was not able to describe an efficient system in place to prevent this type of incident from occurring in the future. She was able to produce an occurrence report. [15] She explained that the allergy section of the care plan was where the most accurate allergy information was kept for all patients, and the allergy to sulfonamides in this case was listed in this section for that particular patient. The surveyor also met with the performance improvement (PI) director and discussed how information about ADRs was collected and used. [16–19]

➔ *Moving Forward.* Based on the tracer, the surveyor may discuss the following in the Daily Briefing: evaluating what medications requiring temperature control nurses transport and store in their cars; whether nurses have adequate knowledge regarding proper storage of medications to protect them from temperature-related degradation; whether nurses are aware of the regulations regarding possession of prescription medications; the communication breakdown between patient care plans and the contracted pharmacy.

Scenario 4-1.
Sample Tracer Questions

The bracketed numbers before each question correlate to questions, observations, and data review described in the sample tracer for Scenario 4-1. You can use the tracer worksheet form in Appendix B to develop a mock tracer (*see* an example of a completed tracer worksheet at the end of this section). The information gained by conducting a mock tracer can help to highlight a good practice and/or determine issues that may require further follow-up.

Nurse:

[1]   Where do you store medications that are transported to and used in patients' homes?

[2]   Do you know if possessing unlabeled prescription drugs is legal in your state? Do you know if organizational policy and/or state law allow you to store and transport medications in your car trunk in such a manner?

[3]   How do you ensure that the medications you transport are kept at proper temperatures?

Patient:

[4]   How is your health now? Have you experienced improvements in your health as a result of the care you have been receiving?

[5]   Did the pharmacy call you and ask about your medication allergies or sensitivities?

[6]   Did you receive any educational materials about medication or learn from your nurse that sulfamethoxazole and trimethoprim were sulfa medications?

[7]   How is assessment information—specifically, medications and patient allergies/sensitivities—shared with the pharmacy?

Pharmacist:

[8]   What processes are in place to validate allergy information for medications that have an increased potential for producing ADRs?

[9]   Does the pharmacy communicate with each patient to verify his or her allergy status?

[10]   How is information on ADRs captured and analyzed by the pharmacy?

[11]   Were processes for validating allergy information and analyzing ADRs followed in this instance?

Nursing Administrator:

[12]   Have you made medication storage a part of your patient/caregiver education? If you have, how do you impart that information?

[13]   Are the nurses allowed by law/regulation to carry emergency medications?

[14]   Do the organization's nurses transport medications requiring temperature control to patients? If so, how are medications stored and protected from temperature-related degradation?

[15]   Walk me through the process used to initiate an occurrence report? What is your involvement in the generation of the report?

PI Director:

[16]   Walk me through the process used to initiate the occurrence report?

[17]   What processes are in place to ensure that all ADRs are captured? How is this capture validated?

[18]   Are there plans to review how information about ADRs is shared with the pharmacy?

[19]   Will the pharmacy be involved in the review and in any subsequent changes/improvements to the system?

SCENARIO 4-2. Hospice
Organization

Summary

In the following scenario, a surveyor conducted a medication management system tracer at a freestanding hospice organization on the home health campus of a large home care company. Within the tracer, the surveyor explored issues relating to these priority focus areas:

- Medication Management
- Organizational Structure
- Information Management
- Assessment and Care/Services

Scenario

The hospice did not have an on-site pharmacy but instead contracted with a local one that was accredited by The Joint Commission. Aware of the relationship between the hospice organization and its contracted pharmacy, the surveyor asked the pharmacist to participate in the hospice organization's medication management tracer. The subsequent roundtable discussion that opened the tracer included the hospice's medical director and two representatives of nursing leadership.

(Bracketed numbers correlate to Sample Tracer Questions on page 86.)

→ *Hearing from the Medical Director.* The medical director shared relevant contracts, including the one between the organization and the pharmacy to provide medications and other pharmaceutical services. The director then shared the organization's written policy describing the minimum information that must be available to those involved in medication management and described the results of a recent self-assessment activity designed to evaluate the accessibility and use of patient information.

After reviewing these foundational elements of the organization's medication management system, the surveyor asked for meeting minutes from an interdisciplinary group meeting held regularly and attended by the medical director, nurses, the chaplain, social workers, and the pharmacist. Minutes from the most recent meeting noted discussion regarding "comfort kits" and the procedures surrounding the ordering process for them, as well as their creation, handling, and dispensing. [1–2] These minutes indicated that hospice patients and their families were experiencing problems with the comfort kits and their contents. This information was of significant interest to the surveyor when considered along with the organization's

other policies. [3–4] The surveyor decided to focus on the use of comfort kits in his medication management tracer.

→ *Talking with the Nurses About Comfort Kits.* In a discussion with the two nurses soon after the introductory roundtable, the surveyor learned that the organization used preprinted order forms to obtain standardized comfort kits from the pharmacy. The surveyor reviewed the forms and asked the nurses how the kits were created for each patient. [5–6] They explained that all the kits were generally alike, containing standardized medications for pain, anxiety, nausea, insomnia, and breathing problems. Beyond this, the kits were customized for each patient, depending on the order. [7] They told the surveyor that some of these medications were controlled substances. Although both nurses were able to describe the state and federal regulations regarding the kits, [8] they could not clearly recite the enhanced medication management activities required for these controlled substances, [9–11] including the education and training delivered to patients. [12–13]

→ *Meeting with the Pharmacist.* Accompanied by the pharmacist, the surveyor next traveled to the pharmacy where he and the pharmacist discussed all aspects of comfort kits. [14–17] The surveyor then reviewed order forms for the kits to confirm the existence of physician signatures and other required information. This information included date signed; patient name and address; name and strength, frequency, route, and quantity of the medication; physician's address; and a Drug Enforcement Agency (DEA) number. These documents were significant in that they allowed the surveyor to check for compliance with law and regulation. [18] They also enabled the surveyor to understand the tracking processes for controlled substance prescriptions implemented by the pharmacy. [19]

The pharmacist told the surveyor that he complied with all applicable state and federal laws and regulations. Nevertheless, the surveyor noted that numerous forms contained incomplete information. When this was pointed out to him, the pharmacist explained that he was aware of the missing elements. He added that he had complied with organization policy requiring him to follow up on instances of missing information in orders with a telephone call to the prescriber for clarification.

→ *Moving Forward.* Based on the tracer, the surveyor may discuss the following in the Daily Briefing: re-examination of policies related to the creation and distribution of comfort kits; remodification of policy to address the expectations of state and federal controlled substances regulations.

Scenario 4-2.
Sample Tracer Questions

The bracketed numbers before each question correlate to questions, observations, and data review described in the sample tracer for Scenario 4-2. You can use the tracer worksheet form in Appendix B to develop a mock tracer (*see* an example of a completed tracer worksheet at the end of this section). The information gained by conducting a mock tracer can help to highlight a good practice and/or determine issues that may require further follow-up.

Medical Director:

[1] Are processes related to comfort kits part of the evaluation of the medication management system?

[2] How does the organization assess whether comfort kits are safe in the patient's home?

[3] What are the policy and processes for the use of comfort kits?

[4] How are staff made aware of DEA and state regulations for the use of comfort kits?

Nurses:

[5] Describe what you know about the ordering and creation of comfort kits.

[6] What is your role in the handling and eventual use of comfort kits?

[7] How are patient needs assessed and documented for comfort kits?

[8] How do you ensure compliance with the regulations?

[9] How is patient compliance with the use of the medications in the kits evaluated?

[10] How is the effectiveness of the kit's medications monitored?

[11] What is done if a patient dies and the comfort kit has not been used?

[12] How are patients/caregivers educated on each medication in the kit?

[13] How is the patient's/caregiver's retention of the educational activities evaluated?

Pharmacist:

[14] How are the kits prepared?

[15] How are the kits ordered?

[16] How are the kits dispensed?

[17] What is done if a patient dies and the comfort kit has not been used?

[18] What procedures are used to ensure that the comfort kits are compliant with DEA and state regulations and organization policy?

[19] Has the tracking process been monitored for diversion and security? Have there been any problems in this area?

SCENARIO 4-3. Hospice Organization

Summary

In the following scenario, a surveyor conducted a medication management system tracer at a hospice organization. Within the tracer, the surveyor explored issues relating to these priority focus areas:

- Medication Management
- Communication
- Patient Safety
- Quality Improvement Expertise/Activities

Scenario

The surveyor began this medication management tracer by reviewing the organization's performance improvement and medication management plans, which had been provided by the hospice director. He asked the director which medications appeared on the organization's high-alert list, as well as how nurses monitored the safety of patients receiving these medications. These questions were answered.

(Bracketed numbers correlate to Sample Tracer Questions on pages 87–88.)

➡ *Document Review with the Hospice Director.* The documentation reviewed by the surveyor indicated that some patients had received inotropic medications, including dopamine, dobutamine, and milrinone. The surveyor asked to see any policies related to these particular medications. [1] The policies presented to him were comprehensive; as a group, they required the inclusion of each patient-candidate's admission criteria, organizational and staff care responsibilities, allowable dosage range, assessment and monitoring criteria, and appropriate nursing visit schedules. Also required was additional training in inotropic therapies for nurses caring for these patients. [2]

The surveyor then selected an 80-year-old male on which to conduct a patient tracer. Having met several of the hospice's criteria for admission, this patient was received one month earlier with a diagnosis of Stage IV (New York Heart Association functional staging) congestive heart failure. Learning that a nurse was scheduled to see this patient, the surveyor requested the opportunity to accompany him.

➡ *Visiting the Patient with the Nurse.* During the drive to the patient's home, the surveyor asked the nurse about the purpose of the visit and for a summary of the patient's condition and care. The surveyor also asked the nurse about his experiences treating patients who, like the man they were about to visit, had received inotropic medications. [3] The nurse explained that he had cared for patients receiving inotropics as part of his hospital experience two years earlier. Since the nurse who regularly cared for this patient was on vacation, he was filling in but had not received additional training in this area as part of his employment with the hospice. [4–5]

The patient had been admitted and discharged from the hospital one week earlier for symptoms related to his congestive heart failure. The nurse and the surveyor found him in good spirits. When asked by the surveyor how the therapy was working for him, the patient indicated that he was very pleased with the care he had received from the hospice nurses. He then shared the events of the previous weekend: Somehow he had run out of the IV dobutamine solution early Saturday morning. He felt fine without the dobutamine until later that night, at which time he called the pharmacy several times but did not receive a response. [6–7] He then called his nurse, who instructed him to obtain dobutamine from the nearest emergency room. Because of his apparent distress, shortness of breath, and edema, he was admitted to the hospital for observation while receiving the drug.

➡ *At the Hospice with the PI Specialist.* Back at the hospice, the surveyor reviewed policies for the treatment of patients receiving inotropic therapies. He asked the performance improvement (PI) specialist for any additional documentation, such as incident reports and any evaluations of the previous weekend's events, pertaining to the tracer patient he had just seen. [8] Although the hospice policy for documenting these events specified a time frame of 72 hours for completion, the PI specialist was not able to provide the occurence report. [9] In fact, none of the evaluative and analytical activities that should have cascaded from the event had been initiated. The monitoring and evaluation of incidents related to patients receiving high-alert medications had not even been identified as a PI priority. [10–12]

The surveyor continued to ask questions about the failure of the on-call process that had resulted in the readmission of the patient to the hospital and about protocols for investigating/evaluating these types of incidents. [13–14] Among other things, the surveyor learned that the pharmacy had not participated in the hospice's evaluation or performance improvement process following this incident.

➡ *Moving Forward.* Based on the tracer, the surveyor may discuss the following in the Daily Briefing: improving the training for nurses who work with patients receiving inotropic medications; establishing a firm organizational policy for the assignment of on-call staff; establishing a firm policy regarding the provision of high-alert medications in the event the pharmacy is unavailable; the investigation of staff failure to follow internal policies and established evaluative and analytical activities.

Scenario 4-3.
Sample Tracer Questions

The bracketed numbers before each question correlate to questions, observations, and data review described in the sample tracer for Scenario 4-3. You can use the tracer worksheet form in Appendix B to develop a mock tracer (*see* an example of a completed tracer worksheet at the end of this section). The information gained by conducting a mock tracer can help highlight a good practice and/or determine issues that may require further follow-up.

Hospice Director:

[1]   Does the assessment/reassessment process/documentation or care plan identify the specific policy requirements for inotropic patients?

[2]   What training is provided for nurses caring for patients receiving inotropic therapies?

Nurse and Patient:

[3]   How are the nurses selected to care for patients receiving high-alert medications?

[4]   What is the process for the provision of additional training and what does this training include? For example, does it include all the components of the hospice's policy?

[5]   How would management know if a nurse without the required training was assigned to care for a patient receiving a high-alert medication?

(continued)

Scenario 4-3.
Sample Tracer Questions (continued)

[6] Is nursing aware of the on-call policies for the pharmacy?

[7] What are the hospice's policies for the provision of inotropic medications in the event the pharmacy does not respond to a patient's or caregiver's call?

PI Specialist:

[8] Is the "high-risk" designation documented in the home care record for patients on high-alert medications?

[9] Are the occurence report submission time frames monitored for timeliness?

[10] How are monitoring priorities chosen for the performance improvement program?

[11] Are adverse events related to high-alert medications considered a priority?

[12] What actions have been taken or are in development to prevent adverse events this from happening again?

[13] What is the organizational policy for the assignment of on-call staff? What alternative policies are in place if the primary on-call pharmacist is unavailable or if there is a malfunction of telephones or other communication equipment?

[14] Does the pharmacy make special provisions for high-risk patients in its on-call process?

SCENARIO 4-4. Hospice Inpatient Facility Pharmacy

Summary

In the following scenario, a surveyor conducted a medication management system tracer at a hospital pharmacy contracted to provide service to a hospice within the hospital. Within the tracer, the surveyor explored issues relating to the following priority focus areas:

- Medication Management
- Equipment Use
- Orientation & Training
- Organizational Structure

Scenario

The surveyor conducted the tracer at a hospice leasing a unit within a hospital and at the hospital pharmacy servicing the

hospice as part of the lease. To garner background, she planned first to talk to the director of the hospice program before speaking with a nurse administrator and then to end with a visit to the on-site pharmacy. In the brief introductory session with the program director, the surveyor was able to review PI data and indicators related to medication management. It was there that the surveyor noticed that medication error rates after hours were double the rates when the pharmacy was open.

(Bracketed numbers correlate to Sample Tracer Questions on page 89.)

➡ *Meeting with the Nurse Administrator.* Sitting down with the nurse leader, the surveyor asked if medications that were not in an automated dispensing machine (ADM) were accessed when the pharmacy was closed between 5:00P.M. and 8:00A.M. [1–2] She specifically asked about the nurses' preparation of sterile IV medications. [3–6] The nurse leader said that nurses commonly retrieved pain medications and IV medications from the pharmacy after the pharmacy was closed. [7–9] Citing the higher error rates during that period, as indicated in the PI data, the surveyor asked how the information was collected and what the organization had done with the data collected.

Acknowledging the problem after-hours access was creating, the nurse said that she had been a member of a departmental team organized over six months previously to address the issue brought to light by the data. [10] The group had developed a list of creative approaches to maintaining after-hours access to a pharmacist for presentation to hospice and hospital management. Some of the ideas included contracting or arranging with a 24-hour pharmacy service for drug information support and creating a "virtual" pharmacy service that would seamlessly provide pharmacist order review, processing, and support from another location linked to the order entry and automated dispensing systems. The nurse pointed out that despite repeated requests for action following the list's submission to management the team had not received a response from management, and it thus had been unsuccessful in resolving the error-rate problem.

➡ *In the Pharmacy.* Moving to the hospital pharmacy, the surveyor questioned the pharmacist specifically about security arrangements for the hours the pharmacy was closed. [11] The pharmacist told the surveyor that the organization maintained a list of medications available to nonpharmacist staff when the pharmacy was closed and that those medications were stored and secured in a night cabinet outside of the pharmacy. He said he knew that nurses sometimes still accessed the pharmacy itself after hours, but he followed organization policy by conducting retrospective reviews of medications dispensed as soon as the pharmacy reopened each day, or as soon as he was available. [12–15]

➡ *Moving Forward.* Based on the tracer, the surveyor may discuss the following in the Daily Briefing: evaluating processes with the goal of reducing or eliminating the occasions in which nonpharmacist health care professionals obtained medications after hours; re-evaluationg the night cabinet system.

Scenario 4-4.
Sample Tracer Questions

The bracketed numbers before each question correlate to questions, observations, and data review described in the sample tracer for Scenario 4-4. You can use the tracer worksheet form in Appendix B to develop a mock tracer (*see* an example of a completed tracer worksheet at the end of this section). The information gained by conducting a mock tracer can help to highlight a good practice and/or determine issues that may require further follow-up.

Nurse Administrator:

[1] When the pharmacy is closed, what are your processes for making sure that a new medication order is properly reviewed prior to administration?

[2] Under what circumstances would a nurse need to call a pharmacist after hours?

[3] What kind of education and training have nurses had on the proper preparation of sterile IV medications? How are competencies assessed?

[4] What is the frequency of these competency assessments?

[5] Does the nurses' orientation include an assessment of the competencies required to prepare sterile IV medications?

[6] Does this orientation address the expectations outlined in the *U.S. Pharmacopedia* (USP) Chapter 797?

[7] What are some of the IV medications nurses prepare after pharmacy hours?

[8] Is there a second person that checks IVs?

[9] Are the IVs prepared fully administered within 12–24

hours?

[10] Has the organization taken steps to resolve the error-rate problem cited in its data? What specifically has taken place?

Pharmacist:

[11] What are the organization's policies for staff entering the pharmacy after hours?

[12] How are medication error data collected?

[13] How are data about medication errors used to improve performance?

[14] What PI initiatives have you done as part of your yearly medication system assessment?

[15] What steps are you taking to evaluate the adequacy of medication supplies for patient care after the pharmacy is closed?

SCENARIO 4-5. Freestanding Infusion Center

Summary

In the following scenario, a surveyor conducted a medication management system tracer at a freestanding infusion center. Within the tracer, the surveyor explored issues relating to these priority focus areas:

- Medication Management
- Communication
- Orientation & Training
- Infection Control
- Assessment and Care/Services
- Equipment Use
- Information Management

Scenario

In this ambulatory infusion center tracer, the surveyor's observations and review of medication administration records revealed that the process to update medication profiles was not conducted per organizational policy. The pharmacy relied on information collected by nurses to perform its pharmaceutical assessment—like height, weight, or possible allergies—to determine possible drug interactions. Spurred by these findings, the surveyor decided to make three observational visits around the infusion center before completing the tracer.

(Bracketed numbers correlate to Sample Tracer Questions at right.)

➡ *Observing a Nurse.* The surveyor observed a nurse preparing an IV therapy solution outside of a sterile preparation area and asked why she prepared the solution in this area. The nurse only responded that she preferred to prepare the medication once the patient arrived to avoid wasting it, as it was very expensive. [1] Later, the surveyor reviewed this nurse's personnel file and noted that it lacked documentation for orientation, training, or competency assessment in the preparation of sterile IV solutions. [2] The surveyor also learned that the organization did not have a specific process that addressed these IV prep activities. [3]

➡ *Speaking with the Pharmacist.* The surveyor followed up on his observation of the nurse's IV preparation by meeting with the pharmacist. The surveyor described what he had observed and asked if the nurse's behavior was indicative of the actions of the nurses in general. [4] The pharmacist told the surveyor it definitely was not and that she could have prepped and provided the IV solution to the nurse within 30 minutes of receiving the order. She added that she did not know why the nurse had bypassed the pharmacy at all. [5]

➡ *Speaking with a Patient.* The surveyor left the pharmacy to talk with the patient who was to receive the IV solution the nurse was preparing. The surveyor asked the patient if he had been informed of the side effects of the medication he was to receive. [6] The patient said he did not recall having received any special instructions or education regarding side effects. [7–8] The surveyor examined the patient's medical record, which indeed did not include documentation of patient education regarding side effects. [9]

➡ *Moving Forward.* Based on the tracer, the surveyor may discuss the following in the Daily Briefing: engaging patients in their care; revieiwng staff education related to medication reconciliation and patient education; reviewing policies for preparation of infusion medications; staff training and assessment.

Scenario 4-5.
Sample Tracer Questions

The bracketed numbers before each question correlate to questions, observations, and data review described in the sample tracer for Scenario 4-5. You can use the tracer worksheet form in Appendix B to develop a mock tracer (*see* an example of a completed tracer worksheet at the end of this section). The information gained by conducting a mock tracer can help to highlight a good practice and/or determine issues that may require further follow-up.

Nurse:

[1] Have you received any training or competency assessment for the sterile preparation of IV medications?

[2] Does the staff personnel file contain documentation of orientation and competency assessment for the preparation of sterile IVs?

[3] What is the organization's policy regarding the preparation of IV therapy solutions outside of the pharmacy? Under the policy, who can prepare these medications, where are they prepared, and under what conditions are they prepared?

Pharmacist:

[4] How can the pharmacy ensure that all medications requiring sterile preparation are prepared in a sterile manner?

[5] How are pharmacy staff involved in the development of medication management policies? How are pharmacy staff involved in nurse's training?

Patient:

[6] What information have you been given regarding the medication you are receiving?

[7] Was the information you received understandable?

[8] Do you have any special communication needs?

[9] How is patient education provided and documented? How are patient's special communications needs met?

SCENARIO 4-6. Infusion Pharmacy

Summary

In the following scenario, a surveyor conducted a medication management system tracer at an infusion pharmacy. Within the tracer, the surveyor explored issues relating to these priority focus areas:

- Medication Management
- Communication
- Orientation & Training
- Infection Control

Scenario

At the opening conference, the surveyor requested the organization's list of high-alert and hazardous medications to help in the selection of tracer patients. After reviewing the list, the surveyor decided to select a patient that was receiving patient-controlled analgesia (PCA). The surveyor would travel with the driver making a delivery of medication to the patient's home.

(Bracketed numbers correlate to Sample Tracer Questions at right and page 92.)

➡ *At the Infusion Pharmacy.* Before departing, the surveyor reviewed the infusion pharmacy's order review, delivery, storage, and disposal policies related to high-alert medications. The surveyor then examined the selected patient's chart to gather additional information such as the patient's special needs, communication level, and availability/quality of home refrigeration, as well as the medication component of the care plan and documentation of execution of the care plan. The surveyor also reviewed the medication profile, medication orders, and medication preparation and distribution documents. [1] In reviewing nursing documentation for the particular patient, the surveyor noted that patient education documentation was missing from the home care record. [2]

➡ *Visiting the Patient with the Driver.* After leaving the pharmacy for the patient's home, the driver told the surveyor that he had received training regarding infection control, emergency management, and medication storage. [3–4] The driver also pointed out that performance evaluations and competency assessments were performed annually and included a ride-along by his supervisor. The surveyor noticed that the van was segregated into clean and dirty areas. A tote box in the van contained legend drugs and other items (IV tubing and infusion devices) that were prohibited by state regulation. [5–6]

Upon arrival at the patient's home, the driver gave the patient her medication and watched as she placed it in her refrigerator. The surveyor noticed that the patient placed the IV bags directly under defrosting hamburger and that fluids from the thawing meat was dripping onto the bags. The driver did not instruct the patient to move the IVs to a different location in the refrigerator. [7] The surveyor also noted that the driver did not use sanitizing gel prior to arriving at the patient's home or later when leaving, though it was stipulated in organization policy. [8]

➡ *Talking with the Patient.* The surveyor talked with the patient about how she had been instructed to store her medication in the refrigerator. [9] The patient said that previously a nurse had instructed her to keep the IVs in the refrigerator and that the nurse had provided written information about the importance of storing it safely. The surveyor then reviewed the medication profile with the patient. This review revealed four medications currently being taken by the patient that were not on the list, along with one medication that had been discontinued four weeks earlier. [10] Before leaving the patient's home, the surveyor asked to see the "welcome packet" containing all documents provided at the start of care. [11–12] The patient could not find the packet.

➡ *Moving Forward.* Based on the tracer, the surveyor may discuss the following in the Daily Briefing: evaluating patient education on medications delivered, including proper storage and sanitary handling; performing organizationwide review of all policies and applicable state regulations.

Scenario 4-6.
Sample Tracer Questions

The bracketed numbers before each question correlate to questions, observations, and data review described in the sample tracer for Scenario 4-6. You can use the tracer worksheet form in Appendix B to develop a mock tracer (*see* an example of a completed tracer worksheet at the end of this section). The information gained by conducting a mock tracer can help to highlight a good practice and/or determine issues that may require further follow-up.

Pharmacy Management:

[1] Is there a policy on patient education regarding medications? If so, how is it documented? How is patient behavior monitored?

[2] Are home care records readily available and kept up to date at all times?

(continued)

Scenario 4-6.
Sample Tracer Questions (continued)

Home Visit Driver:

[3] Do staff training tools address medication storage in general and refrigerated storage specifically?

[4] What training did you receive regarding infection control and hand hygiene policies?

[5] What training did you receive regarding the possession of drug legend items in the delivery vehicle?

[6] Are all medications packaged for individual patients?

[7] What training did you receive regarding medication storage in a patient's home?

[8] How does the organization monitor staff compliance with hand hygiene? Are staff compliant with hand hygiene requirements?

Patient:

[9] Did you receive instructions on how to store your medications safely? Did you receive instructions on how to properly dispose of any wasted medication?

[10] Do you keep a list of the medications you're on? Where is it? How do you keep it current?

[11] Were you provided information about your right to refuse care (for example, to refuse your medications)?

[12] Do you recall receiving any instructions and training regarding use and handling of your medications? For example, do you know why you are taking the medication? Are you aware of its possible side effects? Are you aware of what you should do if you miss a dose?

SCENARIO 4-7. Home Care Agency

Summary

In the following scenario, a surveyor conducted a medication management system tracer at a home care agency. Within the tracer, the surveyor explored issues relating to the following priority focus areas:

- Medication Management
- Assessment and Care/Services
- Communication

Scenario

The surveyor conducted a tracer at a large home care agency that provided home health, pharmacy, and home medical equipment services. The surveyor interviewed the pharmacy director and the performance improvement (PI) specialist and asked them to share any data and indicators they had gathered in regard to medication management.

(Bracketed numbers correlate to Sample Tracer Questions on pages 93.)

→ *Talking with the Pharmacy Director.* The pharmacy director explained that he was part of the agency's medication safety team, which also included the PI specialist, a pharmacy technician, and a nurse. [1] The team's aim, he explained, was to track and implement improvements in medication safety in the organization. The surveyor asked if the organization was focusing on any particular area of medication management. The director explained that the organization had been focusing on reducing falls among patients who were taking medications, [2–3] mindful that fall reduction was the focus of National Patient Safety Goal 9 (*see* Appendix E, page 153). The surveyor and director discussed the initiative further before the surveyor directed questions to the PI specialist. [4–5]

→ *Discussing Falls with the PI Specialist.* In response to questions, the PI specialist explained that nurses conducted medication reconciliation assessments upon the admission of a patient into the home care program and that they reassessed for any further medications at each home visit. [6] This information formed the basis for development of a fall assessment that also involved input from the patient. [7–8] Nurses then shared this information with the pharmacy. [9] These activities were integral to the fall reduction program, the specialist said.

The surveyor asked to review the records of five patients who had recently suffered a fall, which the PI specialist provided. [10] From these records, the surveyor chose that of a 35-year-old who had been administered aminoglycoside and then experienced vertigo and a fall. The record indicated that a fall risk assessment was conducted and that the patient was not deemed a fall risk. A subsequent evaluation of the medical record indicated that the vertigo and the fall were probably due to the gentamicin antibiotic given to this patient for a bone infection. The course of antibiotics was administered over six weeks, and the doses were in the high-normal range. A postfall interview with the patient revealed that the patient had previously experienced severe vertigo. [11]

➡ *Moving Forward.* Based on the tracer, the surveyor may discuss the following in the Daily Briefing: defining the criteria for re-evaluations and documenting when it is completed; continuing the collecting and analyzing of information on adverse events related to falls.

Scenario 4-7.
Sample Tracer Questions

The bracketed numbers before each question correlate to questions, observations, and data review described in the sample tracer for Scenario 4-7. You can use the tracer worksheet form in Appendix B to develop a mock tracer (*see* an example of a completed tracer worksheet at the end of this section). The information gained by conducting a mock tracer can help to highlight a good practice and/or determine issues that may require further follow-up.

Pharmacy Director:

[1]   What steps has the agency taken to improve medication management in regard to patient safety?

[2]   What specific data can you show leading to the decision to focus on patient falls?

[3]   What do your data indicate? Are there opportunities for improvement around fall reduction?

[4]   Describe your fall risk reduction program and how it addresses the potential of certain medications to trigger falls.

[5]   Have you considered developing a formal list of medications associated with falls, like blood pressure medications, sedating medications, diuretics, and analgesics—opiates and muscle relaxants in particular?

PI Specialist:

[6]   When are fall assessments conducted?

[7]   What do you do when you identify a patient to be at risk for falls?

[8]   As part of your assessment process, do you review medication profiles for medications that have the potential to cause falls?

[9]   How is the pharmacy involved in the fall risk reduction program? How do you work with the pharmacy as part of this fall risk reduction program?

[10] How were you trained to assess fall risks?

[11] When there are changes in the patient's condition, how are these considered in a falls re-evaluation?

Sample Tracer Worksheet: Scenario 4-7.

The worksheet below is an example of how organizations can use the sample tracer questions for Scenario 4-7 in a worksheet format during a mock tracer. The bracketed numbers before each question correlate to questions described in the scenario.

A **correct answer** is an appropriate answer that meets the requirements of the organization and other governing bodies. An **incorrect answer** should always include recommendations for follow-up.

Tracer Team Member(s): Theo Washington
Subjects Interviewed: Lon Bukowski, Denise Filmanov
Tracer Topic: Medication-induced patient falls; Leon Derbigny

Data Record(s): Patient records (5), medication management data and indicators
Unit(s) or Department(s): Pharmacy, PI specialist's office, records room

Interview Subject: Pharmacy Director

Questions	Correct Answer	Incorrect Answer	Follow-Up Needed	Comments or Notes
[1] What steps has the agency taken to improve medication management in regard to patient safety?	✓			Organization formed multidisciplinary team that created organization's fall risk reduction program and developed several evidence-based fall risk assessment tools.
[2] What specific data can you show leading to the decision to focus on patient falls?	✓			Organization presented detailed collection data and analysis covering 2.5 years.
[3] What do your data indicate? Are there opportunities for improvement around fall reduction?	✓			Complete analysis of data indicated need for improvement due to history of medication-related falls.
[4] Describe your fall risk reduction program and how it addresses the potential of certain medications to trigger falls.	✓			

Interview Subject: Pharmacy Director (continued)				
Questions	**Correct Answer**	**Incorrect Answer**	**Follow-Up Needed**	**Comments or Notes**
[5] Have you considered developing a formal list of medications associated with falls, like blood pressure medications, sedating medications, diuretics, and analgesics—opiates and muscle relaxants in particular?		✓	Organization should take the next step of compiling this logical information for incorporation into policy.	This seems to be a missing element from the agency's thorough follow-up to its research.

Interview Subject: PI Specialist				
Questions	**Correct Answer**	**Incorrect Answer**	**Follow-Up Needed**	**Comments or Notes**
[6] When are fall assessments conducted?	✓			Medication reconciliation assessments upon admission with follow-up reassessments at each visit are excellent.
[7] What do you do when you identify a patient to be at risk for falls?	✓			Input from at-risk patient included in assessment, plus info shared with pharmacy.
[8] As part of your assessment process, do you review medication profiles for medications that have the potential to cause falls?		✓	Ongoing collection and analysis of information regarding adverse events related to falls needed.	Medication was flagged, but communication with caregiver did not occur.
[9] How is the pharmacy involved in the fall risk reduction program? How do you work with the pharmacy as part of this fall risk reduction program?	✓			Pharmacy was part of multidisciplinary team that created and maintained organization's fall risk reduction program. Performance improvement, nursing, and pharmacy all collaborate.

(continued)

Interview Subject: PI Specialist (continued)				
Question	**Correct Answer**	**Incorrect Answer**	**Follow-Up Needed**	**Comments or Notes**
[10] How were you trained to assess fall risks?	✓			Fall prevention measures are reviewed in the general orientation and in nursing orientation. Nurses complete an assignment in which they complete a risk assessment under the supervision of the nursing director.
[11] When there are changes in the patient's condition, how are these considered in a falls re-evaluation?		✓	Criteria for re-evaluations are poorly defined and not consistently documented as having been completed.	Patient had not been identified at initial assessment as high risk.

Tracer Scenarios for
LONG TERM CARE

NOTE: No Two Tracers Are the Same

Please keep in mind that each tracer is unique. There is no way to know all of the questions that might be asked or documents that might be reviewed during a tracer—or what all the responses to the questions and documents might be. The possibilities are limitless, depending on the tracer topic and the organization's circumstances. These tracer scenarios and sample questions are provided as educational or training tools for organization staff; they are not scripts for real or mock tracers.

Section Elements

This section includes sample tracers—called scenarios—relevant to long term care. The section is organized as follows:

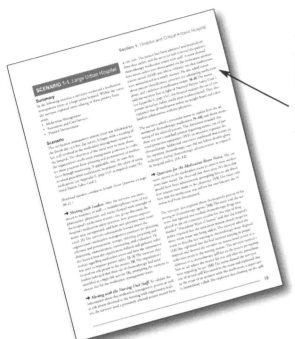

Scenarios: Each scenario presents what might happen when a surveyor conducts a specific type of tracer. The scenarios are presented in an engaging narrative format in which the reader "follows" the surveyor through the tracer scenario. Within the narrative are bracketed numbers that correspond to numbered sample tracer questions following the tracer.

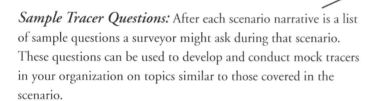

Sample Tracer Questions: After each scenario narrative is a list of sample questions a surveyor might ask during that scenario. These questions can be used to develop and conduct mock tracers in your organization on topics similar to those covered in the scenario.

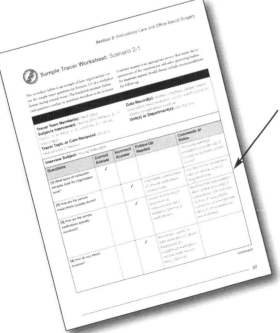

Sample Tracer Worksheet: At the end of the section is a sample worksheet that shows how the sample tracer questions for one select scenario in the section might be used in a worksheet format. The example shows how the worksheet might be completed as part of a tracer for that scenario. A blank form of the worksheet is available in Appendix B.

SCENARIO 5-1. Long Term Care Facility

Summary

In the following scenario, a surveyor conducted a medication management system tracer at a long term care facility. Within the tracer, the surveyor explored issues relating to these priority focus areas:

- Medication Management
- Communication
- Information Management
- Patient/Resident Safety
- Quality Improvement Expertise/Activities

Scenario

The surveyor began the long term care facility site visit by meeting with the facility's director of nursing and the head administrator. The pair described the organization's approach to medication management, specifically telling the surveyor about the organization's medication room storage procedures, medication considerations in disaster situations, medication carts, medication error education, performance improvement program, and medication error identification and reduction processes. They also said that the organization had its own in-house pharmacy and consultant pharmacist in lieu of contracting with an outside pharmacy. At this point, the surveyor was escorted to the facility's pharmacy to meet the pharmacist.

(Bracketed numbers correlate to Sample Tracer Questions at right and on page 100.)

➡ *Talking with the Pharmacist.* At the pharmacy, the surveyor observed the medication and order entry process. [1] The consultant pharmacist explained that all orders were entered as part of a computerized medication distribution system. [2] The sophisticated computer software used for this system displayed screens for many drug parameters, and one of these screens was dedicated to high-alert medications. [3] The surveyor observed the pharmacist entering medications into the system. After noticing her bypass three warnings, the surveyor asked her about the purpose of the alerts. The pharmacist explained that the alerts occurred frequently "for no reason" and that she usually ignored them. [4–5]

➡ *With the Nurse in the Facility.* After the pharmacy visit and following a facility tour and electronic medical records review, the surveyor noted a medication error that had occurred over three weeks earlier. [6–7] A medication had

been entered (handwritten) in the medication administration record (MAR) for a female resident. [8] However, the medication ordered for the woman was not intended for her but instead was meant for her husband, who was assigned to the same room as his wife. [9] The surveyor discussed this error with the residents' nurse, who indicated that the male resident's condition had subsequently worsened and that his wife's overall health had deteriorated as well. [10–14]

➡ *Following Up with the Consultant Pharmacist.* To further investigate the mix-up with the couple's medication order, the surveyor returned to the consultant pharmacist for additional details. [15] The pharmacist could not explain how the order error went undiscovered for almost 30 days. [16–17] She also verified that if the medication order had been entered into the electronic database per policy and not handwritten, the error could have been discovered and prevented. [18–19]

➡ *Moving Forward.* Based on the tracer, the surveyor may discuss the following in the Daily Briefing: the need for greater collaboration between facility staff and the pharmacy; examination of how frequently pharmacy database alerts are bypassed and whether bypasses represent risk points in the medication management system; procedures to ensure use of the MAR according to established policy.

Scenario 5-1. Sample Tracer Questions

The bracketed numbers before each question correlate to questions, observations, and data review described in the sample tracer for Scenario 5-1. You can use the tracer worksheet form in Appendix B to develop a mock tracer (*see* an example of a completed tracer worksheet at the end of this section). The information gained by conducting a mock tracer can help to highlight a good practice and/or determine issues that may require further follow-up.

Consultant Pharmacist:

[1] What high-risk points have you identified in your medication processes?

[2] What is the process for verifying medication orders with medications actually received by residents?

[3] How do you ensure that safe dosing is prescribed for the residents? What do you do if you identify a potentially unsafe dose or medication?

(continued)

Scenario 5-1.
Sample Tracer Questions (continued)

[4]   Do you ever have medication errors or discrepancies that originate in the pharmacy?

[5]   Do you ever experience near misses? If so, do you collect and analyze data regarding those near misses?

Nurse:

[6]   How do you identify medication errors, and how do you report them?

[7]   Do you identify near misses? If so, how are they reported?

[8]   How are orders matched to entries on the MAR?

[9]   How do you document that residents are receiving medications?

[10]   How do you document and report residents' responses to medications?

[11]   Do you educate residents regarding their medications? Do you document this education and the resident's involvement in the medication management program? How do you measure their retention level of these educational activities?

[12]   Is medication safety a component of the orientation received by the nursing staff?

[13]   What two forms of resident identification do you use prior to administration of medication?

[14]   How can this type of error be avoided in the future?

Follow-Up with Consultant Pharmacist:

[15]   How can this type of error be avoided in the future?

[16]   What education activities have been provided for the facility staff? Were they medication-safety related?

[17]   How are training and education regarding the requirements for safe medication management practices provided to staff?

[18]   What priority medication-related processes are you studying to improve safe resident care? Are staff encouraged to report medication errors?

[19]   What improvements have been made to the medication management system? How do you know if they are sustainable?

SCENARIO 5-2. Long Term Care Facility

Summary

In the following scenario, a surveyor conducted a medication management tracer in a long term care facility. Within the tracer, the surveyor explored issues relating to these priority focus areas:

- Medication Management
- Communication
- Orientation & Training
- Patient/Resident Safety
- Quality Improvement Expertise/Activities

Scenario

During the on-site visit, the surveyor explored the medication management process with the facility's director of nursing and the head administrator. The surveyor asked the two leaders about risk points related to medication management. The administrator told him that recent performance improvement activities had focused on increased staff education and patient education, as the organization had determined there was a need in these areas. The director of nursing added that the organization had reviewed National Patient Safety Goal compliance and expert literature related to medication management risk points. The head administrator also added that there had been a few cases of medication noncompliance identified. This, she stressed, was particularly unacceptable.

(Bracketed numbers correlate to Sample Tracer Questions on page 101.)

➜ *Interviewing Residents.* Following up on this last issue, the surveyor reviewed medication dispensing records and conducted resident interviews. During the interviews, many residents indicated that they sometimes felt they needed more medication than was ordered. **[1–2]** They also said that they did not recall receiving any education related to the proper use of their medications or the consequenses of noncompliance. **[3]** Additionally, they said that the medication containers were confusing and difficult to use.

Together, the records and interviews revealed that some residents were not taking their medications at the frequency ordered. This led to diminished general health in some residents' cases and to a surplus of their medications in all cases. It definitely created the potential for preventable medication errors and resultant adverse medication events.

➡ *Speaking with Pharmacy Staff.* When the surveyor approached the pharmacy staff about this situation, [4–6] they said that they had noticed that residents' medications were not always filled at the appropriate frequency but that there was no formal mechanism in place to monitor or determine the extent of this issue. [7–8] The surveyor's review of the pharmacy's performance improvement program showed that the organization did not collect data or monitor the incidence or scope of medication noncompliance by the facility's residents. The pharmacy manager indicated that increased cost prohibited the use of safer medication dispensing systems, such as the punch card (or "bingo card") medication system, which can allow for greater accountability in medication management systems. [9–10]

➡ *Meeting with the Head Administrator.* Later in the tracer, the surveyor once again met with the facility's head adminstrator and questioned her on the compliance issue. [11] The administrator explained that the organization documented resident education and medication compliance in the resident record. [12] Further, staff received quarterly in-service training regarding important medication management policies and procedures, as well as participated in performance improvement activities. The surveyor validated the existence of the in-service staff training, but was unable to find documentation of residents' education regarding their medications. This lack of documentation was consistent with the statements given during the resident interviews.

➡ *Moving Forward.* Based on the tracer, the surveyor may discuss the following in the Daily Briefing: re-examining processes for preparing and dispensing medications, and for administration in particular; collaborating with the pharmacy to monitor and reduce the extent of medication noncompliance; increasing level of staff and resident education.

Residents:

[1] How do you take your medications? As far as you can tell, are the medications delivered in a timely manner? Do you receive them on time—when you need them?

[2] Do staff provide your medications the way your physician has ordered them? If not, can you explain why?

[3] Have you been educated about your medications, how to take them, and what happens when you do not comply with your physician's orders?

Pharmacy Staff:

[4] What processes are in place to reconcile orders with resident compliance?

[5] How are resident medication shortages monitored?

[6] How do you communicate medication shortages to staff?

[7] Explain the process for reviewing all medication orders before each medication is dispensed.

[8] How are residents' medications obtained when the pharmacy is not open around-the-clock?

[9] What packaging methods are utilized for the dispensing of mediations to these residents?

[10] Has the safety of these methods been evaluated?

Head Administrator:

[11] How do you collaborate with the pharmacy to improve the medication compliance of your residents?

[12] What processes are utilized to monitor the compliance or noncompliance with the use of medications by the facility's residents?

Scenario 5-2.
Sample Tracer Questions

The bracketed numbers before each question correlate to questions, observations, and data review described in the sample tracer for Scenario 5-2. You can use the tracer worksheet form in Appendix B to develop a mock tracer (*see* an example of a completed tracer worksheet at the end of this section). The information gained by conducting a mock tracer can help to highlight a good practice and/or determine issues that may require further follow-up.

SCENARIO 5-3. Long Term Care and Subacute Care Facility

Summary

In the following scenario, a surveyor conducted a medication management system tracer at a long term care and subacute care facility. Within the tracer, the surveyor explored issues relating to these priority focus areas:

- Medication Management
- Infection Control
- Orientation & Training

Scenario

The surveyor initiated the tracer with a roundtable discussion that included the director of nursing and the head administrator at the subacute care facility. They addressed the organization's medication management process, and the surveyor asked the leaders for the records of several residents.

(Bracketed numbers correlate to Sample Tracer Questions on page 103.)

→ *At the Medication Cart with a Nurse.* With notes from several residents' records in hand, the surveyor asked the director of nursing to take him to the medication cart so that he could follow up on a specific resident. [1–2] There he was introduced to another nurse who showed him the resident's "bingo card" (punch card) containing one 30-day supply of medication. [3] The nurse also explained the labeling process the organization used to ensure that residents receive the correct dose at the correct intervals for their needs. The surveyor verified that the medications for this resident were labeled and stored correctly and asked the nurse about the types of training and assessment that qualified him to perform his daily tasks. [4]

During this discussion at the medication cart, the surveyor recalled that upon his arrival, the cart was unattended and unlocked in one of the facility hallways. The surveyor had noticed a tablet-crushing device containing tablet powder residue on the top of the cart. The cart also contained multi-dose vials for injections that had been opened but that did not include new beyond-use dates (BUDs). Further, there were intravenous (IV) bags that had been removed from protective overwraps but that also did not include new BUDs.

This prompted the surveyor to ask the nurse to explain organization policy on BUDs. The nurse told the surveyor that normal procedure was to use a pen to record BUDs on opened vials and IVs but that he had not noticed when he came on shift that this had not been done for these medications. Given the BUD variation from organization policy, the surveyor began exploring other areas of the cart. He discovered inhalers and nitroglycerin tablets stored next to topical medications. The surveyor asked if medications in the cart were typically stored this way, and the nurse explained that it was standard practice to store inhalers, tablets, and topical medications together. [5]

The surveyor then indicated the tablet crusher with powder residue on its surface. "Do you have organization-specific policies and procedures regarding the crushing of medications?" he asked the nurse. [6] "The facility does require cleaning the

device between medications and between patients. But I was covering for a nurse who was unexpectedly off duty because of illness and just have not yet had time to clean the thing," he explained.

The surveyor asked the nurse if he had a list of medications that should not be crushed. [7–9] The nurse replied that there was a list at the nurse's station. He was able to produce the list after searching through a procedures binder on a reference shelf at the nurse's station. The surveyor asked if the medication that had been crushed was on the list. The nurse consulted the list and replied that the substance that was crushed was a controlled substance and was on the list of medications that should not be crushed.

→ *In the Pharmacy.* Next, the surveyor talked with the consultant pharmacist about practices for storing medications and how the pharmacy worked with the facility to help ensure that safe practices were followed. [10–13] The pharmacist was not aware of the medication cart issues discovered by the surveyor. The surveyor asked if the pharmacy staff conducted medication room/cart audits to monitor these activities. The pharmacist indicated that they did not conduct such audits, adding that the organziation had recently asked for guidance in replacing medication carts with automated dispensing machines (ADMs). [14]

The surveyor asked if there was training provided by the pharmacy regarding the crushing of medications. The pharmacy acknowledged providing staff with a list of medications that should not be crushed but had not provided education regarding the list. [15–16]

→ *Following Up with the Leaders.* Returning to the two leaders, the surveyor asked the nursing director for the competency assessment and the orientation documents for the nurse he had spoken to earlier. [17] The surveyor thought these documents would help in determining whether the nurse had been adequately oriented and trained and whether he had received competency assessment for issues related to safe storage and administration of medications and infection control issues related to medication storage and administration.

The surveyor also asked the two leaders to share information about how policies and procedures are evaluated against actual practice and about any performance improvement activities with the pharmacy. [18–20] The director and administrator were unable to provide documentation of such a process. They also admitted that they had not worked with the pharmacy to coordinate performance improvement activities, but they felt that it would be an excellent activity to add to the performance improvement program.

→ *Moving Forward.* Based on the tracer, the surveyor may discuss the following in the Daily Briefing: creating and sharing sufficient copies of the do-not-crush medications list to place on all medication carts; educating nursing staff on proper use of the tablet-crushing device and the potential for cross contamination; developing a method to evaluate policies and procedures against actual practice; working with pharmacy staff to develop performance improvement activities.

Scenario 5-3.
Sample Tracer Questions

The bracketed numbers before each question correlate to questions, observations, and data review described in the sample tracer for Scenario 5-3. You can use the tracer worksheet form in Appendix B to develop a mock tracer (*see* an example of a completed tracer worksheet at the end of this section). The information gained by conducting a mock tracer can help to highlight a good practice and/or determine issues that may require further follow-up.

Nurse:

[1] Who can administer medications in the organization?

[2] Are there medications that cannot be administered by a particular class of staff?

[3] How are changes to doses or frequencies made to punch/bingo cards?

[4] Describe the training provided by the organization regarding the handling of the medication cart.

[5] Do you have organization-specific policies regarding the storage of medications? How do you monitor compliance with these policies?

[6] Do you have organization-specific policies and procedures regarding the crushing of medications? Do these policies include instructions for the proper cleaning of the tablet-crushing device?

[7] Does the MAR indicate "do not crush" for medications that should not be crushed?

[8] Has the pharmacy provided in-service training related to medications that should not be crushed?

[9] Does the pharmacy provide a list of "do not crush" medications that can be laminated and attached to the medication cart?

Consultant Pharmacist:

[10] What education has the consultant pharmacist provided regarding the storage of medications?

[11] Is there a standardized monthly review of patient medications by the consultant pharmacist?

[12] Does this review consider duplication of therapy?

[13] What storage policies has the pharmacy developed and implemented? Have they been shared with the facility?

[14] Does the pharmacy work with the subacute care facility on performance improvement activities? Please provide an example.

[15] Does the pharmacy provide a list of "do not crush" medications?

[16] Has the pharmacy provided education programs to the nursing staff regarding the crushing of medications?

Leaders

[17] Describe the medication management and infection control orientation and training that nurses receive, as well as how and how often competency is assessed.

[18] How do you monitor to ensure that policies and procedures are followed? For example, how do you ensure that medications are crushed appropriately and that medications that should not be crushed are not crushed?

[19] Has the pharmacy been asked to join in the performance improvement program to assist in the evaluation of medication management issues, identification of risk points, and their resolution?

[20] Has the pharmacy been asked to provide education or tools to help prevent medication problems?

SCENARIO 5-4. Skilled Nursing Facility

Summary

In the following scenario, a surveyor conducted a medication management system tracer in a skilled nursing facility. Within the tracer, the surveyor explored issues relating to these priority focus areas:

- Medication Management
- Information Management
- Organizational Structure
- Patient/Resident Safety
- Quality Improvement Expertise/Activities
- Physical Environment

Scenario

In a system tracer for medication management, the surveyor asked the nursing director and the head administrator at a skilled nursing facility about adverse drug reactions (ADRs), medication errors, and root cause analysis. The surveyor also reviewed policies in several areas before focusing on how staff worked with the facility's consulting pharmacist to handle resident medications during an emergency.

(Bracketed numbers correlate to Sample Tracer Questions at right and on page 105.)

➡ *Meeting with the Leaders.* The surveyor asked the nursing director if the organization collaborated with its consultant pharmacist on performance improvement (PI) activities. **[1–2]** The administrator replied that it did not but that it was an excellent idea and that the facility would contact the pharmacist to explore areas for future collaboration. The surveyor then asked her how the organization coordinated with the pharmacy in determining where the residents would go if the facility had to be evacuated. **[3–5]** The administrator said that such a policy had called for collaboration with the consultant pharmacist and showed the surveyor a policy covering the evacuation of the facility. The surveyor also asked about the involvement of the internal/dispensing pharmacy staff in the emergency preparedness program. Neither leader could respond but promised to find out.

➡ *Discussing PI with the Consultant Pharmacist.* The surveyor next visited with the consultant pharmacist and discussed the pharmacist's role in the facility's medication management process. **[6]** She told the surveyor that there was a close working relationship between the organization and the phar-

macy and that the pharmacist regularly provided training to facility leadership and staff regarding medication safety and prevention of medication errors. Although education was provided, there were no targeted PI activities either ongoing or pending, she said. **[7]**

On the matter of evacuation, the pharmacist told the surveyor that no specific plans had been made for the delivery of residents' medications if the skilled nursing facility had to be evacuated. **[8]** She said that the organization's leaders had her emergency contact information and that she was confident that they would be able to coordinate residents' medication needs in the event of an evacuation. **[9]**

➡ *Moving Forward.* Based on the tracer, the surveyor may discuss the following in the Daily Briefing: conducting a failure mode and effects analysis to determine how to mitigate the deficits in the medication management processes regarding evacuation and other emergencies; integrating the pharmacy into PI activities.

Scenario 5-4. Sample Tracer Questions

The bracketed numbers before each question correlate to questions, observations, and data review described in the sample tracer for Scenario 5-4. You can use the tracer worksheet form in Appendix B to develop a mock tracer (*see* an example of a completed tracer worksheet at the end of this section). The information gained by conducting a mock tracer can help to highlight a good practice and/or determine issues that may require further follow-up.

Leaders (Nursing Director and Head Administrator):

[1]   How do the consultant pharmacist and the pharmacy participate in the facility's PI program?

[2]   How are ADRs and medication errors tracked in the facility?

[3]   What is the process for ensuring that the residents will continue to receive their medications in an uninterrupted fashion in the event of an evacuation or a disaster?

[4]   What are your expectations of the pharmacy to ensure that medications are provided uninterrupted?

[5]   Have these expectations been communicated to the pharmacy?

SCENARIO 5-5. Skilled Nursing Facility

Summary

In the following scenario, a surveyor conducted a medication management tracer in a skilled nursing facility. Within the tracer, the surveyor explored issues relating to these priority focus areas:

- Medication Management
- Information Management
- Organizational Structure
- Credentialed Practitioners

Scenario

The surveyor began this tracer by asking for a broad overview of the medication management processes at the skilled nursing facility. He then followed up on recent federal regulatory attention to emergency prescription orders and controlled substances for emergency kits, known as "e-kits."

(Bracketed numbers correlate to Sample Tracer Questions on page 106.)

➡ *Talking with the Administrator.* The facility's administrator told the surveyor that she was aware that long term care pharmacies must be equipped to dispense emergency prescription medications to residents 24 hours a day. [1–2] She further explained that these emergency prescription orders included controlled substance pain medications [3] and specially prepared IV antibiotics. All nursing staff were aware of the mandate and the possible consequences of not complying. [4–6] She also explained that the facility's pharmacy had a pharmacist and pharmacy technician on call 24 hours a day to handle urgent requests. The facility and the pharmacy worked together to determine what medications were necessary for the e-kits, and the facility followed state regulatory requirements in determining the com-

position of the kits. The pharmacy was responsible for ensuring that the e-kits were properly stocked to manage emergency situations immediately. The surveyor asked how requirements for controlled substances used for pain management (Schedule II and Schedule III) were addressed. [7] The administrator showed him the organization's written policies and procedures.

➡ *Talking with a Nurse.* After the surveyor left the meeting with the facility administrator, he asked a nurse to show him how she received an order for a resident who needed a controlled substance for emergency pain relief and how she opened an e-kit. [8–9] She first provided the surveyor with examples of how she completed the necessary paperwork, and the surveyor noted that all necessary information about the recipient, dosage, prescriber, and so on was included. The nurse then showed the surveyor how e-kits that were opened and unopened were differentiated. Specifically, a sealed kit had a red plastic security tie and an unsealed kit had a white plastic security tie. The nurse told the surveyor that opened kits were stored in a separate area to be returned to the pharmacy and restocked. [10–11]

➡ *Talking with the Pharmacy Director About E-kits.* Later, the surveyor interviewed pharmacy staff responsible for maintaining the emergency controlled substances boxes [12] and the documentation of physician signatures. The surveyor asked the pharmacy director how the medications removed from the kits were converted into orders and was told that the tracking documents from opened kits were converted into legal, formal orders. [13] A notice was subsequently sent to the physician with the appropriate information, requesting a signature and a return back to the pharmacy within the DEA–required seven days. [14] Later interviews with pharmacy technicians and reviews of pertinent documents, however, revealed that controlled substances were removed from the boxes and physician-signed orders were not obtained by the pharmacy within the federally mandated seven days. [15] Due to the heavy volume of controlled substance usage, the pharmacy director said, the removal tickets were not processed. This created situations in which controlled substances were removed [16–17] without the pharmacy knowing this medication had been removed until the tickets were processed and entered into the system. The surveyor made a note of this 30-day-plus backlog in the processing of these tickets.

➡ *Moving Forward.* Based on the tracer, the surveyor may discuss the following in the Daily Briefing: addressing the issue of e-kit utilization and documentation; leadership, nursing, and pharmacy working together to determine causes of controlled substances removal from e-kits.

Scenario 5-5.
Sample Tracer Questions

The bracketed numbers before each question correlate to questions, observations, and data review described in the sample tracer for Scenario 5-5. You can use the tracer worksheet form in Appendix B to develop a mock tracer (*see* an example of a completed tracer worksheet at the end of this section). The information gained by conducting a mock tracer can help to highlight a good practice and/or determine issues that may require further follow-up.

Administrator:

[1] How does your organization address the need for emergency controlled substances if needed when the pharmacy is closed?

[2] How is this process documented?

[3] What training is provided for nurses regarding organization policy and compliance with federal requirements?

[4] How is the compliance of the nursing staff monitored?

[5] Do you understand the severity of noncompliance for the facility license, your staff and their licensure, and the pharmacy licensure?

[6] Have there been any unresolved discrepancies with controlled medications?

[7] How are requirements for controlled substances for pain management addressed?

Nurse:

[8] What do you do if a resident needs pain relief and the pharmacy is closed?

[9] How do you document the opening of an e-kit and use of a medication?

[10] Explain how e-kits are handled after they are opened.

[11] What orientation and/or education have you received regarding these activities?

Pharmacy Director:

[12] Explain the process for obtaining controlled substances from the emergency controlled substances boxes. How is the process monitored?

[13] What is the process for obtaining the required prescriber signatures? How is the process monitored?

[14] Are these signatures obtained within seven days?

[15] How do you deal with those physicians that do not comply by returning the request signed within the seven days mandated by the DEA?

[16] Are stat pain medications not available to nursing, or are medications being diverted?

[17] Have you had issues with diversion? What do you do to prevent diversion from occuring? How do you monitor for this?

SCENARIO 5-6. Long Term Care Facility

Summary

In the following scenario, a surveyor conducted a medication management tracer in a long term care facility. Within the tracer, the surveyor explored issues relating to these priority focus areas:

- Medication Management
- Equipment Use
- Infection Control
- Patient/Resident Safety
- Information Management

Scenario

The surveyor talked with several leaders of the long term care facility's staff about the organization's medication management process in general before focusing on medication administration and, in particular, infusion pumps. The nursing manager detailed how the organization addressed issues such as labeling, programming, and monitoring of the pumps. She also explained how the nurses and the pharmacy collaborated to ensure that the pumps were operated in a safe manner.

(Bracketed numbers correlate to Sample Tracer Questions on page 107.)

➔ *Discussing Infusion Pumps with Pharmacy Staff.*
At the pharmacy, the surveyor reviewed the processes and documentation for the cleaning, testing, and maintenance of the facility's infusion devices. [1] The surveyor learned that although the infection control issues surrounding the effective cleaning of the devices were reviewed with both nursing and pharmacy staff, the pharmacy staff relied completely on the nursing staff to clean them between uses. [2–3] The surveyor also learned that although both factions of the facility understood that routine maintenance of the pumps must include cleaning, basic safety

checks, and a volumetric accuracy validation, the pharmacy staff did not monitor, track, [4] or document these activities, again trusting the nursing staff to handle them. [5–6]

➡️ *Discussing Infusion Pumps with Nursing Staff.* The surveyor followed up on the investigation with pharmacy staff by interviewing the facility's nursing staff. She asked them about the training they had received in order to operate the pumps [7] and about the processes for routine maintenance. [8] The nurses indicated that the infusion devices were not consistently returned to the pharmacy for routine maintenance, such as cleaning, basic safety testing, and calibration. The same was true for preventive maintenance, which consisted of more extensive testing performed according to manufacturer specifications, at the frequency defined by the manufacturer.

Within the tracer, the surveyor collected serial numbers from several random infusion devices that were being used on facility residents. Using these identifying numbers, the surveyor asked if these particular devices had been cleaned between uses. The nurses were not able to produce documentation of cleaning or other routine maintenance activities for the devices in question. [9] Further, they also could not explain the elements of the process used to perform the basic safety testing for the infusion devices used on their residents. [10–11]

As a final investigatory step, the surveyor returned to the pharmacy to check the infusion device database. She determined that preventive maintenance dates for three of five pumps she had randomly selected in the facility were six months or more past due. [12]

➡️ *Moving Forward.* Based on the tracer, the surveyor may discuss the following in the Daily Briefing: immediately resolving compliance issues related to cleaning, testing, and maintenance of infusion devices.

Scenario 5-6.
Sample Tracer Questions

The bracketed numbers before each question correlate to questions, observations, and data review described in the sample tracer for Scenario 5-6. You can use the tracer worksheet form in Appendix B to develop a mock tracer (*see* an example of a completed tracer worksheet at the end of this section). The information gained by conducting a mock tracer can help to highlight a good practice and/or determine issues that may require further follow-up.

Pharmacy Staff:

[1] What are the routine and preventive maintenance processes for the infusion equipment sent to the long term care facility for use by residents? How are the processes tracked?

[2] Are infusion pumps returned for cleaning between residents? If not, how is routine preventive maintenance performed at the frequencies required?

[3] How are these processes for routine and preventive maintenance for infusion pumps documented?

[4] How are the preventive maintenance frequencies for each infusion pump tracked?

[5] How many assets are beyond their preventive maintenance dates today?

[6] Have any prospective risk analyses been performed on any of the routine or preventive maintenance processes?

Nursing Staff:

[7] Have all nursing staff been provided orientation and education regarding the proper routine maintenance procedures? Is this a component of their competency assessment process?

[8] Explain the equipment management process for the infusion devices used to administer medications to residents.

[9] Are all routine maintenance processes performed between resident use and are they documented?

[10] Has the organization identified the lack of proper device testing as a safety risk?

[11] Has the organization identified the lack of proper cleaning between resident use as an infection control risk?

[12] How are these processes monitored to ensure that policies are followed?

SCENARIO 5-7. Long Term Care Facility

Summary

In the following scenario, a surveyor conducted a medication management system tracer in a long term care facility. Within the tracer, the surveyor explored issues relating to these priority focus areas:

- Medication Management
- Communication

- Organizational Structure
- Patient/Resident Safety
- Quality Improvement Expertise/Activities
- Staffing

Scenario

During the interview with the nursing manager of the long term care facility as part of a medication tracer, the surveyor asked about the services provided by the consultant pharmacist. During their conversation, the nursing manager admitted to an adverse drug event (ADE) months earlier in which a resident was inadvertently given an IV heparin drip. The drug was not prescribed to that recipient but was ordered for another resident.

(Bracketed numbers correlate to Sample Tracer Questions at right and on page 109.)

➡ *Interviewing the Nursing Manager.* Further questioning revealed that the error was soon discovered, but not before the resident experienced a serious adverse effect requiring hospitalization. The manager explained that the consultant pharmacist [1–3] had participated in the subsequent PI process that addressed the reporting and evaluation of adverse events. However, the pharmacist had not completed the occurrence report that would have allowed for a complete review of this incident by the surveyor. [4] When asked, the manager said that completion of this occurence report was required by organization policy. [5]

➡ *Discussing Services and ADEs with the Consultant Pharmacist.* Not long after the discussion with the nurse manager, the surveyor met with the consultant pharmacist. When asked about his role in the facility's medication management process, [6] the pharmacist explained that his responsibility was to ensure safe medication dispensing and appropriate use by reviewing medication therapy and resident history for potential ADRs. [7–9]

He described the policies and procedures for monitoring and reporting ADRs and explained that he reviewed resident charts and visited with residents to monitor their responses to therapy. He routinely shared his findings with the facility's nursing staff. [10] He did all of this in an effort to avoid medication-related problems.

The surveyor then asked the consultant pharmacist about the potential causes of the ADE that the nursing manager had shared. [11–12] The consultant pharmacist explained that a recent staff layoff in pharmacy had doubled the number of resi-

dents he was responsible for monitoring. He said this increase in responsibility had resulted in a lack of proper drug monitoring for several residents, including the one who had required rehospitalization. He admitted that that was most likely a contributing factor in the ADE.

➡ *Interviewing the Pharmacy Manager.* The surveyor concluded the tracer by interviewing the pharmacy manager, who indicated that the number of residents assigned for monitoring by this consultant pharmacist was at the high end of the acceptable range. [13–14] However, the manager said she believed the consultant pharmacist should be able to deal with the responsibilities of monitoring residents at the current work load. [15–16]

➡ *Moving Forward.* Based on the tracer, the surveyor may discuss the following in the Daily Briefing: investigating the exact causes of the ADE via a root cause analysis; re-examining the relationship between nursing staff and pharmacy staff; retraining of the consultant pharmacist.

Scenario 5-7.
Sample Tracer Questions

The bracketed numbers before each question correlate to questions, observations, and data review described in the sample tracer for Scenario 5-7. You can use the tracer worksheet form in Appendix B to develop a mock tracer (*see* an example of a completed tracer worksheet at the end of this section). The information gained by conducting a mock tracer can help to highlight a good practice and/or determine issues that may require further follow-up.

Nursing Manager:

[1] What services does the consultant pharmacist provide?

[2] Are the consultant pharmacist's services performed in a timely manner?

[3] What is your level of satisfaction with the services provided by the pharmacist/pharmacy?

[4] What does the facility expect from the pharmacist regarding ADEs? What does the facility expect regarding coordination of the investigation, analysis and evaluation of results, and corrective action activities?

[5] Has an occurrence report regarding the ADE in question been completed and submitted to you for review?

Consultant Pharmacist:

[6] What clinical responsibilities do you have?

[7] What is the policy for monitoring residents on anticoagulants?

[8] Are standing orders for anticoagulants allowed?

[9] What is the monitoring frequency for anticoagulants?

[10] What is your role in the reporting and analysis of ADEs?

[11] Why do you think the process breakdown leading to the ADE suffered by the resident occurred?

[12] How did patient receive heparin in error?

Pharmacy Manager:

[13] Has your organization established consultant pharmacist-to-resident ratios for monitoring responsibilities?

[14] Are these guidelines followed?

[15] Have occurrence reports regarding the ADE been completed and analyzed?

[16] Was a root cause analysis completed?

SCENARIO 5-8. Long-Stay Nursing Facility

Summary

In the following scenario, a surveyor conducted a medication management system tracer in a long-stay nursing facility. Within the tracer, the surveyor explored issues relating to these priority focus areas:

- Communication
- Medication Management
- Organizational Structure
- Staffing

Scenario

The surveyor met with the nursing facility's leadership group—a consulting clinical pharmacist, nursing director, and medical director—to explore the medication management system and processes for its long-stay population. The facility was a small, 90-bed care center in a rural community. The consulting pharmacist made regular visits to the facility and was also available on call.

(Bracketed numbers correlate to Sample Tracer Questions on page 110.)

Speaking with Leadership. The surveyor asked facility leadership to describe the facility's medication management processes as well as how related data were collected, aggregated, analyzed, and tracked. [1–3] The medical director, who was responsible for the medication management processes, said that she worked with the pharmacist to review medication regimens for residents. She also explained that she and other leaders served on a medication management team that periodically addressed related issues.

The surveyor then asked each member of the group to give his or her perspective on the highest-risk medication management processes in the facility. [4–5] The consulting pharmacist said that he responded to alerts, standards, and other information in the industry regarding high-alert medication management processes. He mentioned, for example, that he was aware of the National Patient Safety Goal related to anticoagulant therapy (*see* Appendix E, page 152). As a result, he explained, one of the high-risk areas he and the rest of the team identified for the facility was warfarin use. The facility tracked adverse drug events (ADEs), pain management, and International Normalized Ratios (INRs) for warfarin use.

The medical director confirmed that warfarin use was a high-risk area for the facility. She also explained that, with the vulnerability of the residents to flu viruses, vaccines and the management of the facility's vaccination program was another area of concern. However, she said that her most pressing concern was the safe management of multiple medication regimens for residents. The nursing director agreed that this was a priority and added that a failure mode and effects analysis (FMEA) indicated that the vast majority of ADEs occurred in residents receiving multiple medications. The surveyor therefore decided to focus on that topic for the remainder of the tracer.

➔ *Reviewing Interventions with the Nursing Director.* The surveyor learned that the facility conducted monthly reviews of any resident on multiple medications and was working to reduce the number of medications administered by employing therapeutic nondrug measures when possible. [6–7] The surveyor then asked the nursing director to further discuss these nonmedication-related therapeutic interventions. [8] The nursing director said that the facility was taking a multidisciplinary approach to this challenge; for example, the facility's dietitian and physical therapist were part of the effort to reduce residents' often complex medication regimens. She led the surveyor to a resident's room and showed him examples of interventions, such as changing a resident's position in bed and darkening a room to relieve pain or discomfort. She also explained that the facility provided training to help staff recognize the value of these new approaches, in addition to their training in medication-related side effects and potential ADEs. [9] The nursing director reported that staff members were gradually accepting the new approach. She added that data tracked since the implementation of the organizationwide effort indicated a reduced rate of ADEs and a successful, safe reduction in the number of complex medications for several residents. [10]

➡ *Touring the Facility with the Pharmacist.* Next, the surveyor toured the facility with the pharmacist. He asked to see the medication storage area. [11] The pharmacist pointed out that high-alert medications, such as warfarin, were identified by clearly distinguishable labels. The surveyor noted that all other medications, including look-alike/sound-alike medications, were also clearly labeled and properly stored. When asked about access to the medications, [12] the pharmacist told the surveyor that, in addition to himself, medical and nursing leadership as well as nursing staff had access to the locked room where medications were stored. The surveyor then asked to see the medication storage cart, which was also properly secured and locked. [13]

The surveyor concluded the tour by visiting the vaccine storage area, where he found vaccines properly stored, with dates and labels, in a refrigerator. [14–15]

➡ *Moving Forward.* Based on the tracer, the surveyor may discuss the following in the Daily Briefing: continuing to work together as a leadership team to address areas of high-risk, perhaps with an outside consultant to advise when there are disagreements about priorities; staff training for any new interventions; looking at the facility's vaccination program in upcoming surveys.

Scenario 5-8.
Sample Tracer Questions

The bracketed numbers before each question correlate to questions, observations, and data review described in the sample tracer for Scenario 5-8. You can use the tracer worksheet form in Appendix B to develop a mock tracer (*see* an example of a completed tracer worksheet at the end of this section). The information gained by conducting a mock tracer can help highlight a good practice and/or determine issues that may require further follow-up.

Leadership:

[1]   What are the facility's medication management processes?

[2]   Who is responsible for overseeing the processes?

[3]   How are medication management data collected, aggregated, analyzed, and tracked?

[4]   What high-risk areas have you identified? How do you identify such areas?

[5]   What is your biggest medication management concern? Explain the tools used to identify, analyze, and track these major areas of concern.

Nursing Director:

[6]   What type of interventions have you implemented to address these high-risk areas? How do you know if the interventions are having the intended effects?

[7]   Describe any education and training provided to staff in relation to such interventions.

[8]   What kind of nonmedication therapeutic interventions are used?

[9]   How have you educated staff on these interventions?

[10] What have been the results of the interventions?

Pharmacist:

[11] Explain how medications are stored and labeled.

[12] Is access to the storage room controlled? If so, how? Who has access?

[13] Where are medication carts kept? How are the carts secured?

[14] Where do you secure and store vaccines?

[15] Describe your vaccination program.

Sample Tracer Worksheet: Scenario 5-4.

The worksheet below is an example of how organizations can use the sample tracer questions for Scenario 5-4 in a worksheet format during a mock tracer. The bracketed numbers before each question correlate to questions described in the scenario.

A **correct answer** is an appropriate answer that meets the requirements of the organization and other governing bodies. An **incorrect answer** should always include recommendations for follow-up.

Tracer Team Member(s): Elbert Savitini
Subjects Interviewed: Dorrie Harmon, Jennifer Angoza, Devon E. Jones
Tracer Topic or Care Recipient: Collaboration with consulting pharmacist during emergencies

Data Record(s): Policy on evacuation of residents in the case of an emergency; general medication-related policies and procedures
Unit(s) or Department(s): Pharmacy

Interview Subject: Leadership

Question	Correct Answer	Incorrect Answer	Follow-Up Needed	Comments or Notes
[1] How do the consultant pharmacist and the pharmacy participate in the facility's PI program?		✓	Establish regular exchange of information related to medication issues (for example, near misses, storage, monitoring) that facilitates performance improvement.	Some organizations have found benefit in coordinating their indicators to discover a greater level of continuity and relevance in their PI activities.
[2] How are ADRs and medication errors tracked in the facility?		✓	Use data on medication errors in education and PI activities.	Although errors are tracked, the data are not shared with staff or included as part of a PI program.
[3] What is the process for ensuring that the residents will continue to receive their medications in an uninterrupted fashion in the event of an evacuation or a disaster? [4] What are your expectations of the pharmacy to ensure that medications are provided uninterrupted? [5] Have these expectations been communicated to the pharmacy?		✓	Work with the pharmacy to develop a detailed plan to order and receive resident medications in the event of an emergency requiring evacuation.	Some long term care facilities and/or pharmacies compile a spreadsheet identifying the locations, contact names, phone numbers, etc., to be used in the event of an evacuation. It may be beneficial for each facility and pharmacy to coordinate emergency preparedness drills or at least invite each other to participate, if possible.

(continued)

Interview Subject: Consultant Pharmacist				
Questions	**Correct Answer**	**Incorrect Answer**	**Follow-Up Needed**	**Comments or Notes**
[6] What is the pharmacy's role in the provision of medication error education?	✓			Pharmacy works closely with organization leadership and staff on known medication safety issues.
[7] How do you participate in the facility's PI program?		✓	Establish regular exchange of information related to medication issues (for example, near misses, storage, monitoring) that facilitates performance improvement.	Pharmacy seems to believe that everything is going well because it has not heard otherwise from the facility.
[8] What is the emergency management plan for monitoring the statuses of residents and their locations in the event of a disaster requiring evacuation?		✓	Work with the facility to develop a detailed plan to order and receive resident medications in the event of an emergency that requires evacuation.	The consultant pharmacist can act as a liaison to share and coordinate the respective emergency preparedness plans.
[9] How would the pharmacy deliver medications to the residents in the event of resident evacuation?		✓	Work with the facility to develop a detailed plan to deliver resident medications in the event of an emergency requiring evacuation.	The respective staffs at both the pharmacy and long term care facility should be educated about the significant components of both plans.

Tracer Scenarios for
INTERNATIONAL

NOTE: No Two Tracers Are the Same

Please keep in mind that each tracer is unique. There is no way to know all of the questions that might be asked or documents that might be reviewed during a tracer—or what all the responses to the questions and documents might be. The possibilities are limitless, depending on the tracer topic and the organization's circumstances. These tracer scenarios and sample questions are provided as educational or training tools for organization staff; they are not scripts for real or mock tracers.

Section Elements

This section includes sample tracers—called scenarios—relevant to international healthcare. The section is organized as follows:

Scenarios: Each scenario presents what might happen when a surveyor conducts a specific type of tracer. The scenarios are presented in an engaging narrative format in which the reader "follows" the surveyor through the tracer scenario. Within the narrative are bracketed numbers that correspond to numbered sample tracer questions following the tracer.

Sample Tracer Questions: After each scenario narrative is a list of sample questions a surveyor might ask during that scenario. These questions can be used to develop and conduct mock tracers in your organization on topics similar to those covered in the scenario.

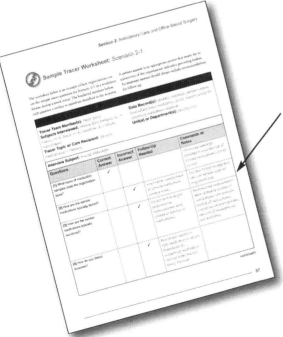

Sample Tracer Worksheet: At the end of the section is a sample worksheet that shows how the sample tracer questions for one select scenario in the section might be used in a worksheet format. The example shows how the worksheet might be completed as part of a tracer for that scenario. A blank form of the worksheet is available in Appendix B.

Tracers Used Internationally

For a brief description of how tracers are used internationally, *see* the "Introduction," page 2.

SCENARIO 6-1. Large Teaching Hospital

Summary

In the following scenario, a surveyor conducted a medication management system tracer in a large teaching care hospital. Within the tracer, the surveyor explored issues relating to quality improvement, storage, staff training, and patient care and safety.

Scenario

The surveyor conducted this medication management system tracer at a 700-bed university hospital. She requested a meeting with the hospital's director of pharmacy, director of nursing, director of quality management, physician members of the pharmacy, members of therapeutics committee, and at least one clinical pharmacist. During this opening session, she asked this leadership group to summarize the process described in the organization's medication management plan, including the organization's annual evaluation of the entire process.

(Bracketed numbers correlate to Sample Tracer Questions on pages 116–117.)

➡ *Meeting with Organizational Leaders.* As part of this discussion, the group of directors, committee members, and the pharmacist described the hospital's implementation of a computerized physician order entry (CPOE) three years ago. Following an initial period of difficulty in convincing physicians to use the system, there was eventually 100% cooperation.

The surveyor asked the group to describe the highest-risk area in their medication management process. [1] They said that chemotherapy was the highest-risk area. Data on near-miss events supported this conclusion, and chemotherapy was the subject of a current proactive risk management analysis that was not yet complete.

The surveyor asked the group how decisions were made about which chemotherapy agents to place on the formulary and to explain requirements for the storage of high-alert medications.

[2–3] Based on the group's responses, the surveyor decided to trace the drug vincristine. Then, the surveyor asked if look-alike/sound-alike medications in the hospital had been identified, [4] as well as how they were stored and labeled.

The surveyor also inquired about risks that may have been incurred due to the organization's change to a CPOE. The answer was somewhat inconsistent. Some among the group felt that not enough attention had been paid to possible new sources of medication errors as a result of this conversion. Eventually, the group told the surveyor that the CPOE came in "a close second" in priority to chemotherapy administration and that it would probably be addressed in the next failure mode and effects analysis (FMEA). Noting this, the surveyor said that she would ensure that this prioritization process would be examined in detail during the improvement of quality and patient safety tracer, although this medication management tracer must focus on one topic.

➡ *In the Pharmacy.* The surveyor toured the pharmacy to observe the storage, labeling, and mixing of medications. [5–6] She asked the pharmacist to demonstrate the entire process, from the receipt of an electronic order all the way through to the release of the medication to the patient care unit. The surveyor noted that chemotherapy drugs were stored in a separate area, [7–8] adjacent to the sterile room where they were mixed, prompting the surveyor to visit that area next. [9] She saw that vincristine was labeled as a look-alike/sound-alike drug, with vinblastine as its pair. The pharmacist explained that the drug was mixed under sterile conditions in a biological safety cabinet. He also said that for the past two months, a second pharmacist had been checking the medication concentration before the medication was released to the nursing unit. [10] The pharmacist explained that he took extra steps to monitor potential adverse drug interactions (ADRs). The surveyor asked the clinical pharmacist to detail the organization's criteria for monitoring and reporting ADRs involving chemotherapy agents, as well as the follow-up process. [11–12]

Before leaving the pharmacy, the surveyor also asked about the training the pharmacist and pharmacy staff received. [13–14]

➡ *Talking to the Oncology Nurse.* When the surveyor finished talking to the clinical pharmacist, she moved to the chemotherapy unit to observe the administration of vincristine. The oncology nurse explained the steps she took to administer the drug, starting with hand hygiene and proper identification of the patient. [15] She showed the surveyor where she documented education of the patient with regard to side effects to be expected [16] and the special flow sheet used for the sequential administration of chemotherapy over a period of time, with tests to monitor effects of the drug on blood count. [17] She told the surveyor that the chemotherapy clinical pharmacist also monitored this process. The surveyor noted the oncology nurse's name and asked that her competency evaluation be available for review during a later session on staff qualification and education.

The surveyor asked the nurse to describe the expected and unexpected ADRs to vincristine in the hospital and after discharge or with outpatient chemotherapy. While in the chemotherapy unit, the surveyor checked the security arrangements for the emergency cart and reviewed the expiration dates of the drugs stored in it. [18]

➔ *With Quality Management.* When the surveyor finished talking to the oncology nurse, she got together with a quality manager. She asked him for data on the frequency and types of medication errors reported during the past six months. [19] When the quality manger provided the data, the surveyor asked whether vincristine was involved in any of these errors. The aggregate report did not specify the drug involved in any of the errors; however, the quality manager showed her data that supported the conclusion that chemotherapy drugs made up a major proportion of medication near misses. [20–21] The quality manager and the surveyor then discussed the current status of the FMEA of chemotherapy administration. [22]

➔ *With the Pharmacy and Therapeutics Committee.* Following the visit to the pharmacy and the oncology unit, the surveyor completed the tracer by again meeting with the pharmacy and therapeutics committee members to close the loop on any questions that resulted from the earlier visits and discussions. She asked whether any medications had been removed from the formulary [23] and discussed how the organization determines which physicians can prescribe chemotherapy drugs. [24] The group also discussed quality improvement. [25]

➔ *Moving Forward.* Based on the tracer, the surveyor may discuss the following in the Daily Briefing: completion of the current proactive risk management analysis; addressing CPOE in the next FMEA; examining of the FMEA prioritization process.

Scenario 6-1.
Sample Tracer Questions

The bracketed numbers before each question correlate to questions, observations, and data review described in the sample tracer for Scenario 6-1. You can use the tracer worksheet form in Appendix B to develop a mock tracer (*see* an example of a completed tracer worksheet at the end of this section). The information gained by conducting a mock tracer can help to highlight a good practice and/or determine issues that may require further follow-up.

Organizational Leaders:

[1] How do you determine high-risk areas in the medication management process?

[2] What process do you follow to add a chemotherapy drug to the hospital formulary?

[3] How and where do you store vincristine and other chemotherapy drugs?

[4] How do you identify look-alike/sound-alike medications?

Clinical Pharmacist:

[5] How do you label the preparations when chemotherapy orders are filled?

[6] What is your role in the management of chemotherapy for oncology patients?

[7] How are supplies stored?

[8] For times when you are short on space and shelving, what other safe and appropriate alternatives have you considered?

[9] Do you use "clean" or "sterile" technique in preparing chemotherapy infusions? Why? Provide a step-by-step description of the way you ensure that mixing occurs under conditions of proper cleanliness.

[10] How and why did you decide that a second person should check the concentration of chemotherapy preparations?

[11] If you find a case of potential adverse drug interaction with diet on one of the nursing units, how do you proceed?

[12] What are your criteria for reporting ADRs involving chemotherapy agents? What is the follow-up process?

[13] How do you determine and ensure required competencies for staff involved in chemotherapy preparation and dispensing?

[14] Tell me about the training you received, including when it was done and when the training was last updated.

Oncology Nurse:

[15] What steps do you take to administer chemotherapy drugs? What steps do you take if some of this medication is spilled on the ground? What if it spills on the patient's skin?

[16] How do you provide education for the patient?

[17] How do you track chemotherapy administration and monitor effects on the patient's blood count?

[18] How do you secure drugs and dispose of expired drugs?

Quality Manager:

[19] What is the hospital's definition of a medication error?

[20] What is the hospital's definition of a near miss?

[21] How are data collected on errors and near misses?

[22] How do you validate the collected data?

Pharmacy and Therapeutics Committee:

[23] Have any medications been removed from the formulary?

[24] How do you determine which physicians can prescribe chemotherapy drugs?

[25] Describe the organization's quality improvement efforts.

SCENARIO 6-2. Ambulatory Care Center

Summary

In the following scenario, a surveyor conducted a medication management system tracer in a large polyclinic with multiple specialty physicians and dentists and an outpatient operating suite. Within the tracer, the surveyor explored issues relating to storage, quality improvement, and patient care and safety.

Scenario

The surveyor discussed the medication management plan and the most recent annual evaluation of the organization's medication management process with the pharmacy director and a physician member of the pharmacy and therapeutics committee.

(Bracketed numbers correlate to Sample Tracer Questions on pages 118–119.)

➜ *Meeting with Director of Quality Management.* Following the session with the pharmacy director and physician, the surveyor met with the hospital's director of quality management. The surveyor learned that the director headed a team that had collected internal data on medication errors throughout the organization. [1–2] After determining their validity, the data were analyzed and the team identified what it considered a medication-related high-risk area: inconsistent documentation of medications ordered and administered in the operating suite and recovery room. [3] The anesthesiologist in charge estimated the need for medications in the operating suite every morning. Medications were delivered in a cart before the first case, and supplemental medications were delivered as needed. After the last case of the day was discharged from the recovery area, the cart with the remaining medications was returned to the pharmacy and restocked. The organization was evaluating a proposal to establish a satellite pharmacy for these areas, but the costs of such a step were determined to be excessive. [4]

➜ *In the Pharmacy.* During a visit to the hospital pharmacy, the surveyor asked one of the pharmacists to explain how she prepared and dispensed the medications ordered by the anesthesiologist, with special attention to how she handled controlled substances. He asked whether any high-alert medications were included in the daily deliveries to the operating suite, and if so, how these were marked. The surveyor also learned the pharmacy's procedure for adding new medications to its formulary. [5]

Upon request, another pharmacist demonstrated the process of dispensing medications to outpatients from receipt of a prescription to release of the medications. The surveyor observed the pharmacist checking the prescription against information about the patient's diagnosis and other medications in the electronic medical record (EMR) to ensure the safety of the prescriptions and then watched the pharmacist fill the prescription. The surveyor asked the pharmacist to explain how she counseled patients when dispensing the medication and what to do if the patient is concerned about privacy during counseling. [6]

When the surveyor checked the refrigerators in the pharmacy, she found proper temperature logs and no expired medications. The surveyor also examined the medication storage areas in the pharmacy. [7–8] The high-alert medications there were clearly identified with colored labels, though the surveyor noticed that some containers held several medications, including some that were not identified on the boxes. A pharmacist told the surveyor he knew this situation posed risks, and he hoped to identify its cause. [9]

In discussing data collection related to medication errors, the pharmacist noted that the number of such events had been steady and that mistaken prescriptions generated through the EMR represented the largest source of errors. No errors had been reported from the operating suite or recovery room areas where the EMR was not in use. **[10]** Analysis indicated that most errors reported were due to physicians overriding the EMR's warning of drug–drug interactions in the preoperative and post-operative phases of care. Peer reviews estimated that at least half of the overrides were clinically justified, however. No errors had been reported from the operating suite or recovery room.

➡️ *Questioning the Physicians.* To further investigate the results of the analysis shared by the pharmacists, the surveyor completed the medication management tracer with a question and answer session with several physicians. This discussion covered the special kinds of orders allowed in the clinic **[11]** and how the physicians' prescriptions complied with organizational policy. **[12]** The group also addressed responsibilities surrounding drug storage on emergency carts **[13]** and the completion of patients' medical records. **[14–15]** The surveyor's diverse inquiries about the introduction of operating suite records into the EMR, **[16]** sustainable improvements to the medication management system, **[17]** and how physician orders were handled by nurses were answered as well. **[18–19]**

➡️ *Moving Forward.* Based on the tracer, the surveyor may discuss the following in the Daily Briefing: an economical alternative to a satellite pharmacy; accurate and complete labeling of boxes containing high-alert medications; periodic review of physicians overriding the EMR's warning of drug–drug interactions.

Scenario 6-2.
Sample Tracer Questions

The bracketed numbers before each question correlate to questions, observations, and data review described in the sample tracer for Scenario 6-2. You can use the tracer worksheet form in Appendix B to develop a mock tracer (*see* an example of a completed tracer worksheet at the end of this section). The information gained by conducting a mock tracer can help to highlight a good practice and/or determine issues that may require further follow-up.

Director of Quality Management:

[1]   Who collects the data for the study of medication errors?

[2]   How do you receive the data? How do you make certain that they are valid and reliable?

[3]   Once the medication error data are analyzed, how do you make certain that those who need to know the results are informed?

[4]   What improvements is the organization working on to reduce medication errors?

Pharmacists:

[5]   What is the process for adding a new medication to the formulary? Can you show me an example of an addition to the formulary during the past year?

[6]   When patients return to refill medications, how do you check with them to find out if they are complying with instructions?

[7]   How often do you check medication storage areas outside the pharmacy?

[8]   Where are sample medications stored?

[9]   If there is no budget for a new storage system in the pharmacy, how will you ensure that all medications are in properly labeled containers?

[10] If you are collecting medication error data primarily through the EMR and if there is a problem of medications given not being recorded in the operating suite and recovery room, how do you know that there have been no medication errors in that area?

Physicians:

[11] What special kinds of orders (range orders, sliding scale, and so on) are allowed in this ambulatory clinic?

[12] How do you ensure that the prescriptions you write comply with the clinic's policy on this subject?

[13] Who determines what medications should be stored in the emergency cart?

[14] Who is responsible for completing the patient's medication list on the medical record? If it is you, how is your performance measured in this matter?

[15] If a patient has an adverse reaction to an injection, how is that noted in the medical record?

[16] Do you plan to incorporate the operating suite and recovery room records into the EMR? If yes, when?

[17] What improvements have been made to the medication management system? How do you know if the improvements are sustainable?

[18] How do nurses receive an order from a physician to administer a medication or a vaccine?

[19] Where do nurses administer medications and vaccines to patients?

SCENARIO 6-3. Medical Transport Organization

Summary

In the following scenario, a surveyor conducted a medication management system tracer in a publicly owned and operated ground ambulance system that served a city of four million located in a subtropical zone. Within the tracer, the surveyor explored issues relating to storage, staff training, quality improvement, and patient care and safety.

Scenario

This medication management tracer began in a conference room at the central dispatch site of a medical transport organization. Two types of transport vehicles, emergency response and nonacute patient transport, were garaged at one central location and at five satellite dispatch locations. Staffing of the vehicles included a driver and paramedic on each trip and a physician or an emergency-qualified nurse on each emergency response call. The organization was managed by the fire department of the municipality.

The surveyor reviewed the organization's medication management plan, along with policies on ordering medications and preparing and storing look-alike/sound-alike medications. In addition, the surveyor requested training records for a physician regarding sedation administration and monitoring; resuscitation training records for a paramedic, nurse, and physician; and a medication error report form.

(Bracketed numbers correlate to Sample Tracer Questions on page 120.)

➡ *Meeting with Key Staff.* The surveyor met with the medical director and consultant pharmacist, as well as a physician, a nurse, a paramedic, and a person primarily assigned to tasks of quality measurement and data analysis. He asked for an explanation of how drugs were selected and procured. [1–2] Following the discussion, the surveyor went to the facility's central drug storage area located on the premises. After inspecting the central stores, the surveyor was able to enter and examine vehicles that stood ready for the next emergency call.

[3] He compared the vehicle's medication inventory to the drugs and intravenous (IV) fluids in the vehicle. [4–7]

➡ *Questions for the Paramedic, Nurse, and Physician.* The surveyor returned to the conference room to meet with the paramedic, the nurse, and the physician. He asked the paramedic questions related to the storage of medications in vehicles [8] and the protocols that govern the use of medications at the site of a vehicular accident. [9–10] The surveyor noted that vehicles were parked outside the dispatch sites, prompting him to ask what was being done to keep medications at temperatures that were safe for the medications within. [11] The paramedic said that the medication bags are kept in an air-conditioned room at the site where they were stored until just before the vehicle left for an emergency call.

In response to other questions, the paramedic explained how he would handle a physician's order received via the vehicle's radio, [12] and addressed queries regarding the documentation of medications used in the field, [13] the collection of data for process improvement purposes, [14] and how transported patients are monitored for the effects of medications given during transport. [15]

Turning to the nurse, the surveyor asked a few questions regarding cardiac emergencies, for example, what she would do if there was a call to the home of a patient suspected of suffering a heart attack. [16–18] Then he asked the physician about the use of sedation for transported patients. [19–21] Finally, he requested data on reported ADRs during transport. [22]

➡ *Discussion with the Quality Specialist and Medical Director.* Toward the end of the tracer, the surveyor discussed medication errors with the quality specialist and the medical director. [23] Noting that data on the subject had been collected for a year, the surveyor asked for the definition of data, for a display of data analysis, and for any conclusions that had been drawn to date on the subject. [24–25] He also took the time to inquire about the competence of the various members of the transport team. [26]

➡ *Moving Forward.* Based on the tracer, the surveyor may discuss the following in the Daily Briefing: other concerns relative to safe storage of the medications in vehicles; medication errors as patients are transferred between hospitals, per transport records.

Scenario 6-3.
Sample Tracer Questions

The bracketed numbers before each question correlate to questions, observations, and data review described in the sample tracer for Scenario 6-3. You can use the tracer worksheet form in Appendix B to develop a mock tracer (*see* an example of a completed tracer worksheet at the end of this section). The information gained by conducting a mock tracer can help to highlight a good practice and/or determine issues that may require further follow-up.

Key Staff:

[1] How is it decided what medications are stocked in the vehicles?

[2] How would a new medication be added to the stock list?

[3] How do you ensure that storage of medications at the dispatch site and in the vehicles meets applicable law and regulation?

[4] Do you have records of your inspection of medication storage at dispatch sites and in vehicles? Let me review the documentation of the most recent inspection.

[5] How do you decide where to obtain the medications that are authorized for use in the field and during transport?

[6] What process do you follow if you learn that a manufacturer has recalled a particular lot of a medication that was being stored and used by the organization?

[7] When was the last time such a recall was issued? How did the process work?

Paramedic, Nurse, and Physician:

[8 How do you ensure that none of the medications you take to the field have expired?

[9] What qualifications do you have for administering medications in the field and during transport?

[10] What steps do you take to start an IV infusion of a patient involved in a vehicular accident?

[11] What do you do if you find medications stored in the vehicle when the temperature outside is over 35 degrees Celsius?

[12] Are you authorized to call the receiving institution to obtain a radio order for medications from a physician? If you are, how do you handle an order that you receive over the radio? How do you document it?

[13] How do you document the medications you administer to a trauma victim in the field?

[14] How have the medication error data collected been used to improve the medication administration process?

[15] How do you monitor a patient for effects of the medications administered during transport?

[16] Are you certified in advanced cardiac life support? If you are certified, what medications may you administer without a physician's order?

[17] Explain how you mix an IV for a cardiac patient and how you administer it.

[18] If you transport a cardiac patient on an emergency call and the patient develops a rhythm problem, how is the decision made to administer anti-arrhythmia drugs?

[19] What special training do you have to qualify you to administer sedation to patients?

[20] What medication is available to reverse sedation, if necessary?

[21] How are patients monitored while sedation is administered?

[22] How have the medication error data collected been used to improve the medication administration process?

Medical Director and Quality Specialist:

[23] What does the analysis show about the possible causes of medication errors?

[24] What are the data collected to measure medication errors? What is the numerator? What is the denominator?

[25] How are the improvements that have been implemented in the medication administration process being monitored?

[26] What is the process for evaluating the competence of physicians, nurses, and paramedics to administer IV fluids in the field? How is the use of sedation by physicians during transport evaluated?

SCENARIO 6-4. Primary Care Center

Summary

In the following scenario, a surveyor conducted a medication management tracer at a community-based primary care center. Within the tracer, the surveyor explored issues relating to storage, staff training, quality improvement, and patient care and safety.

Scenario

The surveyor first reviewed meeting minutes, temperature logs for the vaccine refrigerator, policies on storing medications outside the pharmacy, and policies on writing prescriptions. He was then joined in the center's meeting room by the care center's leadership staff, including several involved in oversight of medication management. The group answered the surveyor's questions regarding the selection and procurement of medications and the planning and evaluation of the center's medication management process. Following this session, the surveyor met one-on-one with the pharmacist.

(Bracketed numbers correlate to Sample Tracer Questions on page 122.)

➡️ *Discussing Issues with the Pharmacist.* Asked what he thought posed the highest risk to safety, the pharmacist said that poor patient compliance with medication instructions was the most common and most serious risk. The practice of physicians providing sample medications to patients without written instructions from him or his staff, he said, was compounding this problem. [1] When the surveyor asked if he had collected any data on this issue, the pharmacist said it was "much too difficult to monitor." [2–3]

Shifting topics, the surveyor asked why the center's documentation did not include a list of high-alert medications, a question the pharmacist could not answer. [4] The surveyor then asked how he differentiated between look-alike/sound-alike medications [5] and how both groups were stored and labeled. [6] The pharmacist said the pairs had been selected, were reviewed at least annually, and were labeled and identified in the pharmacy.

The surveyor pointed out that in conducting individual patient tracers earlier that day, he had observed medication storage on the emergency cart outside the pharmacy. [7] In interviewing physician support staff, he was told they were generally unaware of identified high-alert medications and

look-alike/sound-alike pairs of medications. [8] The emergency cart was to be used only in serious patient emergencies, the pharmacist explained, and in those situations staff simply had to administer what the physician ordered. [9] Otherwise, these medications were all supposed to remain only in the pharmacy. [10] Therefore, no staff education on this topic had been conducted.

At his request, the pharmacist escorted the surveyor to the pharmacy to observe the storage, labeling, and dispensing of medications. [11–12] He asked the pharmacist to demonstrate the entire process, from receipt of a prescription to the release of the medications to the patients. The surveyor then examined the medication storage areas, [13–14] noting that the high-alert medications were clearly identified with colored labels. He also saw that the pharmacy used different-colored labeling on the shelves and boxes for look-alike/sound-alike medications, but learned from the pharmacist that this special labeling was done only in the pharmacy. [15]

➡️ *In the Vaccination Administration Area with a Nurse.* A little later, the surveyor was inspecting the area where the center kept its vaccines. [16] He noticed that while boxes of vaccines were stored in a refrigerator that had a thermometer mounted inside, [17] there were bottles of drinking water in the refrigerator as well. The nurse in charge of vaccinations said that she knew policy required that the storage of medications and food items be kept separate, [18] but she expressed her thought that bottled water was not food and therefore the policy did not apply. Besides, she said, that refrigerator was the only one available on that side of the building. Soon after, the surveyor noticed boxes of injection needles stored directly on the floor. The nurse said that she knew this, too, was not acceptable. She pointed out that it was unavoidable at that time, as the center needed more shelving and more space in general. [19]

The surveyor finished the medication tracer by visiting several physicians' offices and several patient examining rooms to investigate the storage of samples. He also followed up with the administrator/facility manager to explore storage availability. [20]

➡️ *Moving Forward.* Based on the tracer, the surveyor may discuss the following in the Daily Briefing: information provided to patients about medications; data collection on the distribution of sample drugs; establishing an agreed-on list of high-alert medications; staff training on look-alike/sound-alike medications, including their storage and labeling; proper storage of vaccines.

Scenario 6-4.
Sample Tracer Questions

The bracketed numbers before each question correlate to questions, observations, and data review described in the sample tracer for Scenario 6-4. You can use the tracer worksheet form in Appendix B to develop a mock tracer (*see* an example of a completed tracer worksheet at the end of this section). The information gained by conducting a mock tracer can help to highlight a good practice and/or determine issues that may require further follow-up.

Pharmacist:

[1]   What education do patients receive when being provided with sample medications by physicians? Are written instructions provided? How are these things monitored?

[2]   How do you determine whether a medication error has occurred?

[3]   How do you analyze the causes of medication errors?

[4]   How does the organization define high-alert medications?

[5]   What practices are in place to prevent errors due to look-alike/sound-alike medications? How are staff members made aware of these selected medications?

[6]   Have the use of high-alert and look-alike/sound-alike medications been made a part of your policies and procedures?

[7]   Who determines what medications should be stored in the emergency cart?

[8]   How is training provided to staff regarding the requirements for safe storage of look-alike/sound-alike medications?

[9]   How do you ensure that physicians' prescriptions comply with the center's policy on this subject?

[10] How often do you check medication storage areas outside the pharmacy?

[11] Explain how you handle sample medications—from storage to security to distribution to patients.

[12] What are your systems for quality control when medication orders are filled?

[13] What types of medication samples does the organization store?

[14] Where are sample medications stored?

[15] What happens when the organization discovers that medications are not being stored properly?

Nurse:

[16] How do you receive an order from a physician to administer a vaccine?

[17] Are there special requirements for refrigeration temperature documentation for vaccines?

[18] What is the organization's policy on storing vaccines and medications alongside food and beverages?

[19] What other safe and appropriate alternatives have you considered for times when the facility is short on space and shelving?

[20] What improvements have been made to the medication management system? How are these improvements sustained? How do you know they are sustained?

SCENARIO 6-5. Community Hospital

Summary

In the following scenario, a surveyor conducted a medication management tracer at a community-based hospital. Within the tracer, the surveyor explored issues relating to storage, staff training, quality improvement, and patient care and safety.

Scenario

The surveyor conducted this medication management system tracer at a 150-bed community hospital. He asked that the director of the pharmacy and members of the medication management committee to participate in the initial discussion.

(Bracketed numbers correlate to Sample Tracer Questions on page 124.)

→ *Talking with the Medication Management Committee.* In a meeting with the members of the medication management committee and the director of the pharmacy, the surveyor asked questions about the planning of the hospital's medication management process and its annual evaluation, how its medication management plan was formulated, and the details of its monitoring efforts regarding the medication management process. [1]

The surveyor also asked them to identify the area within the hospital's medication management system that they thought offered the highest risk to medication safety. The group said that medication errors had been particularly high the previous year. However, the installation of an automatic dispensing machine (ADM) had had a positive impact on reducing errors since then. [2] Additionally, no data on near-misses had been collected until the ADM's arrival and that the organization was now able to focus on identifying and reporting near-miss events. [3]

At the surveyor's request, the committee then described the hospital's policies for the storage of high-alert medications and said that they had also identified the look-alike/sound-alike medications used throughout the hospital. [4] They detailed how these were safely labeled and stored, as well. The surveyor said that despite this, when he and the other surveyors had conducted individual patient tracers earlier, they had observed medication storage areas on the patient care units. In addition, while interviewing the nurses on the units, he and the other surveyors had observed that they did not seem aware of the identified high-alert medications, nor were they aware which look-alike/sound-alike pairs of medications had been selected. Nursing staff had said that they assumed that was controlled within the ADM system, but they were not aware of any special labeling. [5]

The director of pharmacy said the look-alike/sound-alike pairs had been selected and were reviewed at least annually and that they were labeled and identified in the pharmacy. He described how nursing staff received information regarding the selected pairs and high-alert medications and how medications were segregated within the ADM to help ensure safe dispensing and selection of medications. [6]

At the end of the meeting, based on further discussions about high-alert medications, the surveyor decide to trace unfractionated heparin from the hospital's high-alert list. [7–8]

➡ *In the Pharmacy.* The surveyor next visited the pharmacy to observe the storage, labeling, mixing, and dispensing of the medications there. [9–10] He asked a pharmacist to use a heparin order to demonstrate the entire process, from receipt of an electronic order to release of the medication to the patient care unit. [11–12] The surveyor observed how the pharmacists checked that the medication was ordered for the right patient in the right dose, route, and frequency; how the pharmacy technicians generally filled the order; [13] and how the pharmacists reviewed all the filled orders before dispensing them. The surveyor noted how this system of quality control could effectively identify and catch near misses. [14]

The surveyor continued his tour of the pharmacy and observed the medication storage areas the medication management committee had described earlier. The pharmacy used yellow fluorescent labeling on the shelves and boxes for look-alike/sound-alike medications. Unfractionated heparin and other high-alert medications were identified and stored in separate storage containers. [15] However, the surveyor noticed that the heparin container actually contained other medications that were not identified on the boxes. One of the pharmacists explained they often have "overflow" from higher shelves. [16] She said they had already identified this potential risk and that they conducted frequent checks of the medications stored in each box. She also pointed out that the pharmacy had looked into purchasing other types of storage bins that might prevent this overflow.

The surveyor noted the IV mixing area identified for all sterile mixing. [17] However, he also saw a biological safety cabinet in the room with boxes of diluents stored on top of it, prompting him to ask pharmacy staff if this was acceptable practice. [18] There was definitely a policy against storing anything on top of the cabinets, he was told, but that they were short on storage space and this couldn't be helped. The surveyor saw other boxes stored directly on the floor. Staff said that they knew this was also not acceptable, but again, more space and more shelves were very much needed. [19]

➡ *With the Quality Analyst.* In one of the tracer's final stages, the surveyor met the hospital's quality analyst. He advised the analyst that he would observe the storage and administration of heparin on the nursing units as part of a later individual patient tracer. He would also query the nurses on their use of the ADM a bit later. He then asked for data on the frequency and types of medication errors that had been reported over the past six months. [20–22] When presented with the data, the surveyor asked whether heparin was involved in any of these errors. The quality analyst stated that the answer would require an examination of the individual medication error reports because the aggregate report did not specify the drug involved in the error. [23]

➡ *Moving Forward.* Based on the tracer, the surveyor may discuss the following in the Daily Briefing: staff training on high-risk and look-alike/sound-alike medications, including their storage and labeling; a better system for identifying specific types of drugs involved in medication error reports.

Scenario 6-5.
Sample Tracer Questions

The bracketed numbers before each question correlate to questions, observations, and data review described in the sample tracer for Scenario 6-5. You can use the tracer worksheet form in Appendix B to develop a mock tracer (*see* an example of a completed tracer worksheet at the end of this section). The information gained by conducting a mock tracer can help to highlight a good practice and/or determine issues that may require further follow-up.

Medication Management Committee:

[1]   What improvements have been made to the medication management system in the past year? How are these improvements sustained? How do you know they are sustained?

[2]   What happens with medication error data? Have you seen any changes when a medication error is identified?

[3]   What happens after your organization identifies a near miss? Is a root cause analysis performed?

[4]   What high-alert and look-alike/sound-alike medications and processes have been identified?

[5]   How do you ensure that staff members are made aware of requirements for safe practices?

[6]   Describe specifically how the ADM helps your particular organization practice safe medication practices. Do you maintain data on errors before and after instituting an ADM?

[7]   How are staff made aware of the medications identified as high alert? How are high-alert medications stored and labeled to ensure safe practice?

[8]   How did you decide that unfractionated heparin is a high-alert medication identified for this hospital? How did you decide which of the various heparin preparations should be available in this hospital?

Pharmacy Staff:

[9]   How are training and education provided to pharmacy staff regarding the requirements for safe dispensing of medications?

[10]   How do you determine and ensure required competencies for your staff?

[11]   Are you aware of any adverse drug reaction reports concerning the use of heparin this past year? If so, what follow-up has been done?

[12]   How did you select the vendor for heparin?

[13]   What is the role of the pharmacy technician in your pharmacy? What competencies are required?

[14]   What are your systems for quality control when medication orders are filled?

[15]   Show me how and where you store heparin and other high-alert medications in the pharmacy.

[16]   If you are short on space and shelving, what other safe and appropriate alternatives have you considered?

[17]   How and where are sterile preparations mixed?

[18]   How should supplies and medications be stored?

[19]   How do you ensure compliance with defined processes? Discuss training regarding proper storage of medications. Show me the attendance record of pharmacists at the medication storage training session.

Quality (or Risk) Management:

[20]   What is the organization's definition of a medication error?

[21]   What is the definition of a near miss?

[22]   How are data collected on errors and near misses?

[23]   Have you submitted your data for analysis? If so, may I see the results of the analysis?

SCENARIO 6-6. Long Term Care Facility

Summary

In the following scenario, a surveyor conducted a medication management system tracer at a long term care facility. Within the tracer, the surveyor explored issues relating to storage, quality improvement, staff training, and patient care and safety.

Scenario

The surveyor conducted this medication management system tracer at a 70-bed community long term care facility. The residents of this facility were primarily elderly individuals with chronic medical and neurological conditions. The surveyor first organized and led a group discussion with the medical director, the nursing director, and the pharmacist. They were soon joined by the quality improvement manager.

The group responded to the surveyor's queries about the organization's selection and procurement of medications, the monitoring and evaluation of its medication management process, and its requirements for the storage of high-alert medications, including the criteria used for identifying high-alert drugs. This last issue caught the surveyor's attention in particular. During individual patient tracers as part of the regular survey, she had examined medication storage on the nursing units and had found no special labeling of medications that were typically listed as high-alert.

(Bracketed numbers correlate to Sample Tracer Questions on page 126.)

→ *Meeting with the Pharmacist.* Following the group session, the surveyor met one-on-one with the pharmacist and asked questions about the organization's storage and labeling of both high-alert and look-alike/sound-alike medications. The pharmacist said that pairs of look-alike/sound-alike medications had been selected, were reviewed at least annually, and were labeled and identified in the pharmacy. The same procedures had been used for high-alert drugs as well, and nursing staff received information regarding both. [1] In fact, the pharmacist added, he helped host an in-service education session on the subject a year earlier. [2] The surveyor next asked who ensured that medications were safely stored in nurse's stations. The pharmacist replied that because he was part-time, he had no time to oversee that activity.

The surveyor was then provided the opportunity to tour the pharmacy to observe the storage, labeling, and mixing of all medications. She asked the pharmacist to demonstrate the entire process of sending medications to the nursing units—from receipt of an order [3–5] through its release to the unit. The pharmacist said that he dispensed medications twice a week, based on a transcribed summary order sheet submitted by the nurses from the facility's two resident care units. If a medication was needed on other days—for example, for newly admitted residents or others already in the facility, the resident's physician had to write a prescription or call an outside pharmacy. [6–7] The family would then deliver the medication to the nurse, who would give it to the patient. [8]

The surveyor also inspected the area identified for mixing IVs. She noticed that there was no laminar flow hood in this area. On being questioned about how the mixing took place, the pharmacist stated that specially trained nurses, who underwent competency testing for this skill once a year, handled that. [9] The surveyor also asked for data on the frequency and types of medication errors that were reported over the preceding six months. [10] The report provided showed virtually no errors over the six months since data collection began. [11–13]

→ *Visiting the Nursing Unit.* Next, the surveyor visited a nursing unit to observe the storage of medications there [14] and to review the transcription of physicians' orders for medications. The medications were all in one overfilled cabinet. She noted several shelves on which medications were stored in bins assigned to individual patients. [15] Some bins were stored behind each other, and there were instances of two medications in the same bin. [16] The surveyor saw three vials of injectable medications that were past their expiration dates. [17] There was an emergency kit stored in the room as well that contained several injectable medications. None of these injectables showed expired dates. [18] The kit did include a list of its contents with daily checks to verify that the kit was complete. [19]

At the surveyor's request, a nurse on duty showed her the unit's refrigerator where other stock medications were stored. It had a temperature chart on it that indicated daily temperature readings. These reading were within the expected range every day for the previous month, except for three consecutive days when the temperature exceeded 9 degrees Celsius. [20] There was no notation to explain the reason for this, nor what was done to remedy it.

The nurse explained that for refills of patients' medications [21] or for medications ordered to be begun on the days the pharmacist was available, there was a clipboard containing a Pharmacy Requisition Form. [22] The nurse on the night shift on Sundays and Wednesdays was responsible for completing it. The next morning, the form would be submitted to the pharmacy, and the nurse would receive the drugs labeled for individual patients that afternoon. [23]

→ *Moving Forward.* Based on the tracer, the surveyor may discuss the following in the Daily Briefing: labeling of high-alert medications; review of IV mixing area requirements; remedies for variations in refrigeration temperatures.

Scenario 6-6.
Sample Tracer Questions

The bracketed numbers before each question correlate to questions, observations, and data review described in the sample tracer for Scenario 6-6. You can use the tracer worksheet form in Appendix B to develop a mock tracer (*see* an example of a completed tracer worksheet at the end of this section). The information gained by conducting a mock tracer can help to highlight a good practice and/or determine issues that may require further follow-up.

Pharmacist:

[1]   Are you aware of any adverse drug reaction reports concerning the use of high-alert medications in the past year? If so, what follow-up has been done?

[2]   What is the content of the education that is provided to staff regarding high-alert medications?

[3]   How are you informed of who is authorized to order medications in this facility?

[4]   If a physician orders a medication that is not stocked in the pharmacy, what is the procedure for handling this situation?

[5]   How do you handle a situation in which a medication is recalled by the manufacturer? Can you recall medications from the nursing units?

[6]   What is the facility's policy on allowing physicians to call in medication orders by telephone?

[7]   Are you aware of any limitations on physicians' prescribing in this facility? If so, what are those limitations?

[8]   When families bring medications to be administered to patients, how do you make certain that the medications are safe to use?

[9]   How do you ensure that information given during in-service education is retained by the nursing staff for a year or more?

[10]   What is the facility's definition of a medication error?

[11]   What is its definition of a near miss?

[12]   How are data collected on errors and near misses?

[13]   Do you believe that the data you have collected so far on medication errors are accurate? Why or why not? What steps will you take next in exploring medication errors?

Nurse:

[14]   How should medications be stored?

[15]   If the pharmacist is unable to oversee medication storage on the nursing units, what alternative way do you ensure proper storage of medications?

[16]   When you are short on space for medication storage, what other safe and appropriate alternatives have you considered?

[17]   How do you make sure that the medication stocks in nursing units do not contain expired medications?

[18]   What is the facility's policy on medications that are about to expire?

[19]   How is it determined what medications should be stocked in the emergency kits?

[20]   What is the process to use when you find that the temperature in the refrigerator exceeds the safe level?

[21]   When you get a verbal or telephone order for a medication, what is the process of recording it?

[22]   When you receive a Pharmacy Requisition Form, how do you make certain that it is requesting the right medication for the right patient?

[23]   What improvements have been made to the medication management system in the past year? How are these improvements sustained? How do you know they are sustained?

Sample Tracer Worksheet: Scenario 6-4.

The worksheet below is an example of how organizations can use the sample tracer questions for Scenario 6-4 in a worksheet format during a mock tracer. The bracketed numbers before each question correlate to questions described in the scenario.

A **correct answer** is an appropriate answer that meets the requirements of the organization and other governing bodies. An **incorrect answer** should always include recommendations for follow-up.

Tracer Team Member(s): Bob Mansirotti Jr.
Subjects Interviewed: Dr. Jomo Mbeki, Alfredo Lorenzo, Lena Romo,
Tracer Topic or Care Recipient: Sample medications, medication storage, vaccine storage

Data Record(s): Meeting minutes, temperature logs, look-alike/sound-alike medication list, medication storage policies, written prescription policies
Unit(s) or Department(s): Pharmacy, vaccination administration area, physicians' offices, examination rooms

Interview Subject: Pharmacist

Questions	Correct Answer	Incorrect Answer	Follow-Up Needed	Comments or Notes
[1] What education do patients receive when being provided with sample medications by physicians? Are written instructions provided? How are these things monitored?		✓	Examine and if necessary, update organization policy on sample distribution procedures. Seek input from pharmacy staff on methods to strengthen monitoring aspect. Review orientation and training, as well as procedural manuals.	Physicians may need in-service training on policy, especially regarding providing instructions with all samples.
[2] How do you determine whether a medication error has occurred?		✓	Interview pharmacy, medical, and nursing staff regarding awareness of error reporting requirements and systems. Develop more proactive, comprehensive methods to capture errors, adverse drug events, and near misses.	Error reports seem to focus only on administration errors. In addition, organization relies solely on incident reporting.
[3] How do you analyze the causes of medication errors?		✓	Ask those involved in the error to participate in analysis and share information about errors (or near misses) with clinical leaders so that issues can be resolved before occurring elsewhere.	Data on administration errors have been collected, but no analysis has been done.

(continued)

Interview Subject: Pharmacist (continued)				
Questions	**Correct Answer**	**Incorrect Answer**	**Follow-Up Needed**	**Comments or Notes**
[4] How does the organization define high-alert medications?		✓	Pharmacy must be part of a multidisciplinary team to create and maintain high-alert medication list.	
[5] What practices are in place to prevent errors due to look-alike/sound-alike medications? How are staff members made aware of these selected medications?	✓			
[6] Have the use of high-alert and look-alike/sound-alike medications been made a part of your policies and procedures?	✓		Need to establish a defined source list for high-alert medications.	Defined source list for look-alike/sound-alike medications exists and has been made a part of practice.
[7] Who determines what medications should be stored in the emergency cart?	✓			
[8] How is training provided to staff regarding the requirements for safe storage of look-alike/sound-alike medications?		✓	Pharmacy to develop and lead interdisciplinary workshop regarding look-alike/sound-alike medications, including safe storage. Compliance to be monitored through random spot checks.	List is generated but does not seem to be a working document—no awareness of list or re-evaluation of list.
[9] How do you ensure that physicians' prescriptions comply with the center's policy on this subject?	✓			
[10] How often do you check medication storage areas outside the pharmacy?		✓	As noted above, pharmacy to lead interdisciplinary workshop regarding high-alert medication processes, including storage of look-alike/sound-alike medications.	Clinical care staff seem to see high-alert medication processes as the sole responsibility of pharmacy rather than as an organization-wide effort.

Interview Subject: Pharmacist (continued)				
Questions	**Correct Answer**	**Incorrect Answer**	**Follow-Up Needed**	**Comments or Notes**
[11] Explain how you handle sample medications—from storage to security to distribution to patients.	✓		Weak point in adherence to procedures seems to be at the physician level.	
[12] What are your systems for quality control when medication orders are filled?	✓			Bar-coding system in place.
[13] What types of medication samples does the organization store?	✓			
[14] Where are sample medications stored?	✓			All samples remain under the control of the pharmacy to ensure inventory integrity. Sample storage areas are routinely inspected for expired medications, samples stored in the wrong place, drugs that cannot be identified, and so forth.
[15] What happens when the organization discovers that medications are not being stored properly?	✓			Staff appear diligent in following appropriate storage procedures. Organization leaders appear consistent in addressing issues immediately.

Interview Subject: Nurse				
Questions	**Correct Answer**	**Incorrect Answer**	**Follow-Up Needed**	**Comments or Notes**
[16] How do you receive an order from a physician to administer a vaccine?	✓			Nurse clearly explained policy and procedure.
[17] Are there special requirements for refrigeration temperature documentation for vaccines?	✓			Clear policy is in place. Suggest all staff review.

(continued)

Interview Subject: Nurse (continued)

Questions	Correct Answer	Incorrect Answer	Follow-Up Needed	Comments or Notes
[18] What is the organization's policy on storing vaccines and medications alongside food and beverages?		✓	Need to review the policy on vaccine/medication storage. Review policy with all staff handling vaccine/medication.	Center should consider acquiring additional refrigerator for staff-only use.
[19] What other safe and appropriate alternatives have you considered for times when the facility is short on space and shelving?		✓	Initiate process improvement team with pharmacy to address medication storage issues.	Pharmacy staff have been awaiting management decision on its request for additional space.
[20] What improvements have been made to the medication management system? How are these improvements sustained? How do you know they are sustained?		✓	Work more closely with quality improvement to monitor data for evidence of sustained improvement and actual reduction in specific medication error elements.	The main improvement implemented has been the labeling of look-alike/sound-alike drugs in the pharmacy. No studies of the effects of this improvement have been done.

Appendix A Priority Focus Areas

Priority Focus Areas

At the beginning of each tracer scenario in this workbook is a brief summary that includes the priority focus areas (PFAs) that are focused on in the scenario. The PFAs are processes, systems, or structures in a health care organization that significantly impact safety and/or the quality of care provided. There are 14 PFAs that are generally universal across health care settings. All Joint Commission standards are related to PFAs. During the on-site survey process, surveyors link the PFAs within standards compliance issues to identify potential areas of risk. The PFAs, along with clinical/service groups (CSGs) from the Priority Focus Process (PFP), form the foundation of the tracer process. The CSGs categorize care recipients and/or services into distinct populations for which data can be collected. The PFP is a data-driven tool that helps focus survey activity on issues most relevant to care recipient safety and quality of care at the specific health care organization being surveyed.

The PFAs are summarized in the following sections.

Analytic Procedures

The laboratory's main function is that of conducting preanalytic, analytic, and postanalytic procedures. NOTE: This PFA is applicable to Laboratory accreditation programs only.

Subprocesses for Analytic Procedures include the following:
- Request
- Specimen collection
- Transportation
- Receipt
- Processing
- Testing
- Interpretation of results
- Data report/dissemination

Assessment & Care/Services

Assessment & Care/Services for care recipients comprise the execution of a series of processes that are fluid in nature to accommodate needs of care recipients including, as relevant, screening; assessment; planning care, treatment, and/or services; provision of care; ongoing reassessment of care; and discharge planning, referral for continuing care, or discontinuation of services. Although some elements of Assessment & Care/Services may occur only once, other aspects may be repeated or revisited as the care recipient's needs or care delivery priorities change. Successful implementation of improvements in Assessment & Care/Services relies on the full support of leadership.

Subprocesses of Assessment & Care/Services include the following:
- Screening
- Assessment
- Planning care, treatment, or services
- Provision of care, treatment, or services
- Reassessment
- Discharge planning or discontinuation of services

Communication

Communication is the process by which information is exchanged between individuals, programs/services, or organizations. Effective Communication successfully permeates every aspect of a health care organization, from the provision of care to performance improvement, resulting in a marked improvement in the quality of care delivery and functioning.

Subprocesses of Communication include the following:
- Provider– and/or staff–care recipient communication
- Care recipient and family education
- Staff communication and collaboration
- Information dissemination
- Multidisciplinary teamwork

Credentialed Practitioners

Credentialed Practitioners are health care professionals whose qualifications to provide care, treatment, and services have been verified and assessed, resulting in the assignment of clinical responsibilities. The Credentialed Practitioners category varies from organization to organization and from state to state. It includes licensed independent practitioners and others who are permitted to provide care, treatment, and services to care recipients under the direction of a sponsoring physician. Licensed independent practitioners are permitted by law and the health care organization to provide care, treatment, and services without clinical supervision or direction within the scope of their license and consistent with individually assigned clinical responsibilities or individually granted privileges.

Equipment Use

Equipment Use incorporates the selection, delivery, setup, and maintenance of equipment and supplies to meet the needs of care recipients and staff. It generally includes movable equipment, as well as management of supplies that staff members use (for example, gloves, syringes). (Equipment Use does not include fixed equipment such as built-in oxygen and gas lines and central air conditioning systems; such items are included in the Physical Environment PFA.) Equipment Use includes planning and selecting; training and orientation; maintaining, testing, and inspecting; educating and providing instructions; delivery and setup; and risk prevention related to equipment and/or supplies. NOTE: This PFA is not applicable to Behavioral Health Care accreditation programs.

Subprocesses of Equipment Use include the following:
- Selection
- Maintenance strategies
- Periodic evaluation
- Orientation and training

Infection Control

Infection Control includes the prevention, surveillance/identification, and control of infections among care recipients, employees, physicians and other licensed independent practitioners, contract service workers, volunteers, students, and visitors. Infection Control is a systemwide, integrated process that is applied to all programs, services, and settings.

Subprocesses of Infection Control include the following:
- Prevention and control
- Surveillance/identification
- Reporting
- Measurement

Information Management

Information Management is the interdisciplinary field concerning the timely and accurate creation, collection, storage, retrieval, transmission, analysis, control, dissemination, and use of data or information, both within an organization and externally, as allowed by law and regulation. In addition to written and verbal information, supporting information technology and information services are also included in Information Management.

Subprocesses of Information Management include the following:
- Planning
- Procurement
- Implementation
- Collection
- Recording
- Protection
- Aggregation
- Interpretation
- Storage and retrieval
- Data integrity
- Information dissemination

Medication Management

Medication Management encompasses the systems and processes used to provide medication to individuals served by the organization. This is usually a multidisciplinary, coordinated effort of health care staff who implement, evaluate, and constantly improve the processes of selecting, procuring, storing, ordering, transcribing, preparing, dispensing, administering (including self-administering), and monitoring the effects of medications throughout the care recipients' continuum of care. In addition, Medication Management involves educating care recipients and, as appropriate, their families about each medication, its administration and use, and potential side effects. NOTE: This PFA is not applicable to Laboratory accreditation programs.

Subprocesses of Medication Management include the following:
- Selection
- Procurement
- Storage
- Prescribing or ordering
- Preparing
- Dispensing
- Administration (including self-administration)
- Monitoring

Organizational Structure

Organizational Structure is the framework for an organization to carry out its vision and mission. The implementation is accomplished through corporate bylaws and governing body policies, organization management, compliance, planning, integration and coordination, and performance improvement. Organizational Structure includes the organization's governance, as well as business ethics, contracted organizations, and management requirements.

Subprocesses of Organizational Structure include the following:
- Management requirements
- Corporate bylaws and governing body plans
- Organization management
- Compliance
- Planning
- Business ethics
- Contracted services

Orientation & Training

Orientation is the process of educating newly hired staff in health care organizations to organizationwide, department-, program-, service-, and job specific competencies before they provide care, treatment, or services to care recipients. Newly hired staff includes, but is not limited to, regular staff employees, contracted staff, agency (temporary) staff, float staff, volunteer staff, students, housekeeping, and maintenance staff.

Training refers to the development and implementation of programs that foster staff development and continued learning, address skill deficiencies, and thereby help ensure staff retention. More specifically, training entails providing opportunities for staff to develop enhanced skills related to revised processes that may have been addressed during orientation, new care techniques for care recipients, or expanded job responsibilities. Whereas orientation is a one-time process, training is a continuous one.

Subprocesses of Orientation & Training include the following:
- Organizationwide orientation
- Program/service orientation
- Job-specific orientation
- Training and continuing or ongoing education

Patient Safety

Patient Safety entails a framework for proactively identifying the potential and actual risks to safety, identifying the underlying cause(s) of the potential or actual risk, and making the necessary improvements to reduce risk. It also entails establishing processes to respond to sentinel events, identifying risks through root cause analysis, and making necessary improvements. This involves a systems-based approach that examines all activities within an organization that contribute to maintaining and improving care recipient safety, including performance improvement and risk management, to ensure that the activities work together, not independently, to improve care and safety. This systems-based approach is driven by organization leadership; anchored in the organization's mission, vision, and strategic plan; endorsed and actively supported by medical staff and nursing leadership; implemented by directors; integrated and coordinated throughout the organization's staff; and continuously re-engineered using proven, proactive performance improvement modalities. In addition, effective reduction of errors and other factors that contribute to unintended adverse outcomes in an organization requires an environment in which care recipients, their families, and organization staff and leaders can identify and manage actual and potential risks to safety.

Subprocesses of Patient Safety include the following:
- Planning and designing services
- Directing services
- Integrating and coordinating services
- Reducing and preventing errors
- Using *Sentinel Event Alerts*
- The Joint Commission's National Patient Safety Goals
- Clinical practice guidelines, if available
- Actively involving care recipients in their care, treatment, or services

Physical Environment

The Physical Environment refers to a safe, accessible, functional, supportive, and effective physical environment for care recipients, staff members, workers, and others by managing physical design; construction and redesign; maintenance and testing; planning and improvement; and risk prevention, defined in terms of utilities, fire protection, security, privacy, storage, and hazardous materials and waste. The Physical Environment may include the home in the case of in-home programs and foster care.

Subprocesses of Physical Environment include the following:
- Physical design
- Construction and redesign
- Maintenance and testing

- Planning and improvement
- Risk prevention

Quality Improvement Expertise/Activities

Quality Improvement Expertise/Activities identifies the collaborative and interdisciplinary approach to the continuous study and improvement of the processes of providing health care services to meet the needs of consumers and others. Quality Improvement Expertise depends on understanding and revising processes on the basis of data and knowledge about the processes themselves. Quality Improvement involves identifying, measuring, implementing, monitoring, analyzing, planning, and maintaining processes to ensure they function effectively. Examples of Quality Improvement Activities include designing a new service, flowcharting a clinical process, collecting and analyzing data about performance measures or care recipient outcomes, comparing the organization's performance to that of other organizations, selecting areas for priority attention, and experimenting with new ways of carrying out a function.

Subprocesses of Quality Improvement Expertise/Activities include the following:

- Identifying issues and establishing priorities
- Developing measures
- Collecting data to evaluate status on outcomes, processes, or structures
- Analyzing and interpreting data
- Making and implementing recommendations
- Monitoring and sustaining performance improvement

Rights & Ethics

Rights & Ethics includes care recipient rights and organizational ethics as they pertain to the care of care recipients.

Rights & Ethics addresses issues such as care recipient privacy, confidentiality, protection of health information, advance directives (as appropriate), organ procurement, use of restraints, informed consent for various procedures, and the right to participate in care decisions.

Subprocesses of Rights & Ethics include the following:

- Care recipient rights
- Organizational ethics pertaining to care recipient care
- Organizational responsibility
- Consideration of care recipient
- Care sensitivity
- Informing care recipients and/or family

Staffing

Effective Staffing entails providing the optimal number of competent personnel with the appropriate skill mix to meet the needs of a health care organization's care recipients based on that organization's mission, values, and vision. As such, it involves defining competencies and expectations for all staff (the competencies of licensed independent practitioners and medical staff are addressed in the Credentialed Practitioners PFA for all accreditation programs). Staffing includes assessing those defined competencies and allocating the human resources necessary for care recipient safety and improved care recipient outcomes.

Subprocesses of Staffing include the following:

- Competency
- Skill mix
- Number of staff

Appendix B   Mock Tracer Worksheet Form

You can use the worksheet on the following pages to record information during a mock tracer. Make as many extra copies of the second page as needed. Below are explanations of terms on the worksheet.

Worksheet Terms

- **Mock Tracer Name:** Give your mock tracer a name for easy reference. This may be as simple as Mock Tracer 1.

- **Date(s) Conducted:** Indicate the date(s) on which the mock tracer took place.

- **Tracer Team Member(s):** List the person or people performing the tracers in the surveyor role.

- **Subjects Interviewed:** List all the people who were interviewed during the entire tracer.

- **Tracer Topic or Care Recipient:** Note the topic or care recipient traced by the person or people performing the surveyor role in the mock tracer. You may also think of it as the focus of the mock tracer.

- **Data Record(s):** List any documents—paper or electronic—consulted during the mock tracer.

- **Unit(s) or Department(s):** List all places visited during the mock tracer. They should conform to the places where the in-

terview subjects work or were encountered during the tracer.

- **Interview Subject:** Fill in the name of the person interviewed. If the person is a member of the staff or administration, add his or her job title as well.

- **Questions:** Record each question asked of the particular interview subject. You might want to use some of the sample tracer questions from the scenarios in this workbook for mock tracers with a similar focus to those scenarios.

- **Correct Answer and Incorrect Answer:** Check the appropriate column to indicate whether the interview subject provided a correct or incorrect answer. A **correct answer** is an appropriate answer that meets the requirements of the organization and other governing bodies. An **incorrect answer** should always include recommendations for follow-up.

- **Follow-Up Needed:** When the interview subject gives an incorrect answer, specify follow-up. This may be recommendations for further evaluation of an issue, staff education, or even another mock tracer.

- **Comments or Notes:** Add anything else you need to remark on. Use this spot as a place to record positive impressions for correct answers as well.

Mock Tracer Name: Date(s) Conducted: Tracer Team Member(s): Subjects Interviewed:		Tracer Topic or Care Recipient: Data Record(s): Unit(s) or Department(s):		
Interview Subject:				
Questions	**Correct Answer**	**Incorrect Answer**	**Follow-Up Needed**	**Comments or Notes**

Interview Subject:				
Questions	Correct Answer	Incorrect Answer	Follow-Up Needed	Comments or Notes

Interview Subject:				
Questions	Correct Answer	Incorrect Answer	Follow-Up Needed	Comments or Notes

Appendix C

Comprehensive Organization Assessment Form

You can use this form as a tool to help define the topics and scope of mock tracers for your organization.

Area of Assessment and Related Questions	Response
Scope and Overall Structure • What is the size and scope of your organization? Are you large, medium, or small? • What is the general structure of your organization—are you private, not-for-profit, educational? • What services do you provide? What population(s) do you serve? • What level of care do you provide?	
Condition of Resources • What types of resources are available in your organization? • Would you describe your organization as resource-rich or resource-poor? • How easily can new funds be made available for new projects, such as mock tracers? • What is the general time frame needed to request and receive resources for new initiatives?	
Size and Complexity — Administrative Structure • Are you a facility-based organization? • Are you a multisite organization that provides more than one level or type of care in more than one type of setting and that requires the use of standards and elements of performance from at least two accreditation manuals? • Are you part of a health care system? • If you have many sites, how far apart are they? • Does each site require extensive travel to reach it? • Does each site have a stand-alone department or staff designated to perform quality improvement activities, or are those activities centralized in one "corporate" location or headquarters?	

(continued)

Area of Assessment and Related Questions	Response
Staff Experience, Training, and Resources • How well-seasoned are the staff in your organization? • Do you have a mix of experienced and newer staff? • What types of staff positions do you have in your organization? • Do you need a lot of training on basic quality improvement concepts or are you well versed and well trained?	
Data Collection and Analysis • What types of data do you collect in your organization? • What departments, areas, or units collect data? • Who in your organization collects data? • What area of the organization is responsible for gathering and studying the data? • What types of external sources of data do you report to or gather data from? • What benchmarking, if any, do you use? • How do you track data and collect them? • Do you use any electronic system for data collection and analysis? If so, who is trained to use it?	
Staff Expertise • Do you have any staff with accreditation survey experience? • If not, how do you prepare for accreditation surveys? • Do you have any staff on site with expertise in data analysis? • If not, how do you analyze your organization's data?	
Safety Concerns • Are there any areas of concern related to the delivery of safe, high-quality care that have emerged in the organization? • Are there any systems or processes that leadership would like to study and assess? • Have any external data pointed to areas of concern that might benefit from a tracer?	

Area of Assessment and Related Questions	Response
Near Misses and Sentinel Events • Has the organization experienced any recent near misses or sentinel events that point to any breakdowns in processes or systems that would benefit from tracer work?	
High-Risk Processes and Concerns • What, if any, high-risk processes and concerns exist in your organization? • How have those high-risk processes been identified?	
Staff Strengths and Expertise • Have you conducted an assessment of the overall skills and expertise that staff bring to the organization? • Do any staff members possess training or expertise in such areas as facilitation, education, training, systems thinking, or other areas that could be helpful in conducting tracers?	
Policies and Procedures Related to Care, Treatment, or Services • Is there ready access to the policies and procedures in the organization? • How often are policies and procedures reviewed and updated in the organization?	

Appendix D Medication Management Standards

DOMESTIC (U.S.) STANDARDS

Planning	HAP/CAH	AHC/OBS	BHC	OME	LTC
Standard MM.01.01.01					
The [organization] plans its medication management processes. [**BHC Note:** *This standard is applicable to organizations that engage in any of the medication management processes.*]	X	X	X	X	X
Standard MM.01.01.03					
The [organization] safely manages high-alert and hazardous medications. [**BHC Note:** *This standard is applicable to organizations that engage in any of the medication management processes.*]	X	X	X	X	X
Standard MM.01.01.05					
The organization monitors the use of psychotropic medications.			X		X
Standard MM.01.02.01					
The [organization] addresses the safe use of look-alike/sound-alike medications.	X	X	X	X	X
Selection and Procurement	**HAP/CAH**	**AHC/OBS**	**BHC**	**OME**	**LTC**
Standard MM.02.01.01					
The [organization] selects and procures medications. [**BHC Note:** *This standard is applicable only to organizations that operate a pharmacy.*]	X	X	X	X	X

HAP = hospital accreditation program	BHC = behavioral health care accreditation program
CAH = critical access hospital accreditation program	OME = home care accreditation program
AHC = ambulatory care accreditation program	LTC = long term care accreditation program
OBS = office-based surgery accreditation program	

(continued)

Storage	HAP/CAH	AHC/OBS	BHC	OME	LTC
Standard MM.03.01.01					
The [organization] safely stores medications. [**BHC Note:** *This standard is applicable only to organizations that store medications at their sites.*]	X	X	X	X	X
Standard MM.03.01.03					
The [organization] safely manages any emergency medications.	X	X	X	X	X
Standard MM.03.01.05					
The [organization] safely controls medications brought into the [organization] by [**HAP/CAH, AHC/OBS, OME: patients; BHC: individuals served; LTC: residents**], their families, or licensed independent practitioners. [**BHC Note:** *This standard is applicable only to organizations that administer medications in their own facility.*]	X	X	X	X	X
Ordering and Transcribing	**HAP/CAH**	**AHC/OBS**	**BHC**	**OME**	**LTC**
Standard MM.04.01.01					
Medication orders are clear and accurate.	X	X	X	X	X
Preparing and Dispensing	**HAP/CAH**	**AHC/OBS**	**BHC**	**OME**	**LTC**
Standard MM.05.01.01					
The [organization] [HAP/CAH, OME, LTC: A pharmacist] reviews the appropriateness of all medication orders [OME: or prescriptions] for medications to be dispensed in the [organization]. [**BHC Note:** *This standard is applicable only to organizations that operate a pharmacy.*]	X	X	X	X	X
Standard MM.05.01.07					
The [organization] safely prepares medications [**BHC:** for administration]. [**AHC/OBS, BHC, LTC Note:** This standard is applicable to all organizations that prepare medications for administration.]	X	X	X	X	X

Preparing and Dispensing (continued)	HAP/CAH	AHC/OBS	BHC	OME	LTC
Standard MM.05.01.09					
Medications are labeled. **[AHC/OBS, OME Note:** *This standard is applicable to all organizations that prepare medications for administration.*] **[BHC Note:** *This standard is applicable only to organizations that dispense or administer medications.*]	X	X	X	X	X
Standard MM.05.01.011					
The [organization] safely dispenses medications. **[BHC Note:** *This standard is applicable only to organizations that operate a pharmacy.*] **[LTC Note:** *This standard applies to all organizations, whether they have an on-site pharmacy or contract for pharmacy services.*]	X	X	X	X	X
Standard MM.05.01.13					
The [organization] safely obtains medications when the pharmacy is closed. **[BHC, LTC Note:** *This standard is applicable only to organizations that operate a pharmacy.*]	X		X	X	X
Standard MM.05.01.15					
The [organization] safely obtains medications when it does not operate a pharmacy. **[BHC:** For organizations that do not operate a pharmacy but administers medications: The organization safely obtains prescribed medications.]	X (CAH only)	X	X	X	X
Standard MM.05.01.17					
The [organization] follows a process to retrieve recalled or discontinued medications. **[BHC:** Organizations that operate a pharmacy or distribute sample medications follow a process to retrieve recalled or discontinued medications.] **[AHC/OBS Note:** *This standard is applicable to all organizations that dispense medications, including sample medications.*]	X	X	X	X	X

(continued)

Preparing and Dispensing (continued)	HAP/CAH	AHC/OBS	BHC	OME	LTC
Standard MM.05.01.19					
The [organization] safely manages [**BHC:** unused, expired, or] returned medications. [**BHC Note:** *This standard is applicable only to organizations that administer medications.*]	X	X	X	X	X
Administration	**HAP/CAH**	**AHC/OBS**	**BHC**	**OME**	**LTC**
Standard MM.06.01.01					
The [organization] safely administers medications. [**BHC Note:** *This standard is applicable only to organizations that administer medications.*]	X	X	X	X	X
Standard MM.06.01.03					
Self-administered medications are administered safely and accurately. [**OME:** Medications are safely and accurately administered by patients and families. [**Note:** *The term self-administered medication(s) may refer to medications administered by a family member.*]	X		X	X	X
Standard MM.06.01.05					
The [organization] safely manages investigational medications. [**BHC Note 1:** *This standard is applicable only to organizations that use investigational medications.* **Note 2:** *Refer to the Glossary for the definition of investigational medications.*]	X	X	X	X	X
Monitoring	**HAP/CAH**	**AHC/OBS**	**BHC**	**OME**	**LTC**
Standard MM.07.01.01					
The [organization] monitors [**CAH, AHC/OBS, OME:** patients; **BHC:** individuals served; **LTC:** residents] to determine the effects of their medication(s). [**BHC Note:** *This standard is applicable only to organizations that prescribe or administer medications.*]	X (CAH only)	X	X	X	X

Monitoring (continued)	HAP/CAH	AHC/OBS	BHC	OME	LTC
Standard MM.07.01.03					
The [organization] responds to actual or potential adverse drug [**BHC:** medication] events, significant adverse drug [**BHC:** medication reactions], and medication errors. [**BHC Note 1:** *This standard is applicable only to organizations that prescribe or administer medications.* **Note 2:** *See the Glossary for definitions of "adverse medication event" and "significant adverse medication reaction."*]	X	X	X	X	X
Evaluation	**HAP/CAH**	**AHC/OBS**	**BHC**	**OME**	**LTC**
Standard MM.08.01.01					
The [organization] evaluates the effectiveness of its medication management system. **Note 1:** *This evaluation includes reconciling medication information. (Refer to NPSG.03.06.01 for more information)* [**BHC Note 2:** *This standard is applicable only to organizations that prescribe, dispense, or administer medications.*]	X	X	X	X	X

(continued)

INTERNATIONAL (JCI) STANDARDS*

Organization and Management
Standard MMU.1
Medication use in the organization complies with applicable laws and regulations and is organized to meet patient needs.
Standard MMU.1.1
An appropriately licensed pharmacist, technician, or other trained professional supervises the pharmacy or pharmaceutical service.
Selection and Procurement
Standard MMU.2
An appropriate selection of medications for prescribing or ordering is stocked or readily available.
Standard MMU.2.1
There is a method for overseeing the organization's medication list and medication use.
Standard MMU.2.2
The organization can readily obtain medications not stocked or normally available to the organization or for times when the pharmacy is closed.
Storage
Standard MMU.3
Medications are properly and safely stored.
Standard MMU.3.1
Organization policy supports appropriate storage of medications and applicable nutrition products.
Standard MMU.3.2
Emergency medications are available, monitored, and safe when stored out of the pharmacy.
Standard MMU.3.3
The organization has a medication recall system.
Ordering and Transcribing
Standard MMU.4
Prescribing, ordering, and transcribing are guided by policies and procedures.

* From *Joint Commission International Accreditation Standards for Hospitals,* 4th Edition

Ordering and Transcribing (continued)
Standard MMU.4.1
The organization defines the elements of a complete order or prescription and the types of orders that are acceptable for use.
Standard MMU.4.2
The organization identifies those qualified individuals permitted to prescribe or to order medications.
Standard MMU.4.3
Medications prescribed and administered are written in the patient's record.
Preparing and Dispensing
Standard MMU.5
Medications are prepared and dispensed in a safe and clean environment.
Standard MMU.5.1
Medication prescriptions or orders are reviewed for appropriateness.
Standard MMU.5.2
A system is used to dispense medications in the right dose to the right patient at the right time.
Administration
Standard MMU.6
The organization identifies those qualified individuals permitted to administer medications.
Standard MMU.6.1
Medication administration includes a process to verify the medication is correct based on the medication order.
Standard MMU.6.2
Policies and procedures govern medications brought into the organization for patient self-administration or as samples.
Monitoring
Standard MMU.7
Medication effects on patients are monitored.
Standard MMU.7.1
Medication errors, including near misses, are reported through a process and time frame defined by the organization.

Appendix E

NATIONAL PATIENT SAFETY GOALS (NPSGs)

National Patient Safety Goal 1:

Improve the accuracy of [HAP/CAH, AHC/OBS, OME: patient identification; LTC: resident identification; BHC: the identification of individuals served].

NPSG.01.01.01	HAP/CAH	AHC/OBS	BHC	OME	LTC
Use at least two [**HAP/CAH, AHC/OBS, OME:** patient; **LTC:** resident] identifiers when providing care, treatment, [**HAP/CAH, AHC/OBS:** and; **BHC:** or] services. [**BHC Note:** *Treatments covered by this goal include high-risk interventions and certain high risk medications (for example, methadone). In some settings, use of visual recognition as an identifier is acceptable. Such settings include those that regularly serve an individual (for example, therapy) or serve only a few individuals (for example, a group home). These are settings in which the individual stays for an extended period of time, staff and populations served are stable, and individuals receiving care are well-known to staff.*] [**LTC Note:** *At the first encounter, the requirement for two identifiers is appropriate; thereafter, and in any situation of continuing one-on-one care in which the clinician knows the resident, one identifier can be facial recognition.*] [**OME Note:** *In the home care setting, patient identification is less prone to error than in other settings. At the first encounter, the requirement for two identifiers is appropriate; thereafter, and in any situation of continuing one-on-one care in which the clinician "knows" the patient, one of the identifiers can be facial recognition. In the home, the correct address is also confirmed. The patient's confirmed address is an acceptable identifier when used in conjunction with another individual-specific identifier.*]	X	X	X	X	X
NPSG.01.03.01	**HAP/CAH**	**AHC/OBS**	**BHC**	**OME**	**LTC**
Eliminate transfusion errors related to patient misidentification.	X	X			

See Appendix D Key on page 143 for a list of program names.

(continued)

National Patient Safety Goal 2:					
Improve the effectiveness of communication among caregivers.					
NPSG.02.03.01	**HAP/CAH**	**AHC/OBS**	**BHC**	**OME**	**LTC**
Report critical results of tests and diagnostic procedures on a timely basis.	X				

National Patient Safety Goal 3:					
Improve the safety of using medications.					
NPSG.03.04.01	**HAP/CAH**	**AHC/OBS**	**BHC**	**OME**	**LTC**
Label all medications, medication containers, and other solutions on and off the sterile field in perioperative and other procedural settings. **Note:** *Medication containers include syringes, medicine cups, and basins.*	X	X			
NPSG.03.05.01	**HAP/CAH**	**AHC/OBS**	**BHC**	**OME**	**LTC**
Reduce the likelihood of patient harm associated with the use of anticoagulant therapy. **Note:** *This requirement applies only to [organizations] that provide anticoagulant therapy and/or long-term anticoagulation prophylaxis (for example, atrial fibrillation) where the clinical expectation is that the patient's laboratory values for coagulation will remain outside normal values. This requirement does not apply to routine situations in which short-term prophylactic anticoagulation is used for venous thrombo-embolism prevention (for example, related to procedures or hospitalization) and the clinical expectation is that the patient's laboratory values for coagulation will remain within, or close to, normal values.*	X	X			X
NPSG.03.06.01	**HAP/CAH**	**AHC/OBS**	**BHC**	**OME**	**LTC**
Maintain and communicate accurate patient medication information.	X	X	X	X	X

National Patient Safety Goal 7:

Reduce the risk of health care–associated infections.

NPSG.07.01.01	HAP/CAH	AHC/OBS	BHC	OME	LTC
Comply with either the current Centers for Disease Control and Prevention (CDC) hand hygiene guidelines or the current World Health Organization (WHO) hand hygiene guidelines. [**BHC Note:** *This standard applies only to organizations that provide physical care.*]	X	X	X	X	X

NPSG.07.03.01	HAP/CAH	AHC/OBS	BHC	OME	LTC
Implement evidence-based practices to prevent health care–associated infections due to multidrug-resistant organisms in critical access hospitals. **Note:** *This requirement applies to, but is not limited to, epidemiologically important organisms such as methicillin-resistant staphylococcus aureus (MRSA), clostridium difficile (CDI), vancomycin-resistant enterococci (VRE), and multidrug-resistant gram-negative bacteria.*	X				

NPSG.07.04.01	HAP/CAH	AHC/OBS	BHC	OME	LTC
Implement evidence-based practices to prevent central line–associated bloodstream infections. **Note:** *This requirement covers short- and long-term central venous catheters and peripherally inserted central catheter (PICC) lines.*	X				X

NPSG.07.05.01	HAP/CAH	AHC/OBS	BHC	OME	LTC
Implement evidence-based practices for preventing surgical site infections.	X	X			

National Patient Safety Goal 9:

Reduce the risk of patient harm resulting from falls.

NPSG.09.02.01	HAP/CAH	AHC/OBS	BHC	OME	LTC
Reduce the risk of falls.				X	X

(continued)

National Patient Safety Goal 14:

Prevent health care–associated pressure ulcers.

NPSG.14.01.01	HAP/CAH	AHC/OBS	BHC	OME	LTC
Assess and periodically reassess each resident's risk for developing a pressure ulcer and take action to address any identified risks.					X

National Patient Safety Goal 15:

The organization identifies safety risks inherent in [HAP/CAH, AHC/OBS: its patient population; BHC: the population of the individuals it serves; LTC: its resident population].

NPSG.15.01.01	HAP/CAH	AHC/OBS	BHC	OME	LTC
Identify patients at risk for suicide. [**HAP Note:** *This requirement applies only to psychiatric hospitals and patients being treated for emotional or behavioral disorders in general hospitals.*]	X (HAP only)		X		

NPSG.15.02.01	HAP/CAH	AHC/OBS	BHC	OME	LTC
Identify risks associated with home oxygen therapy such as home fires.				X	

Universal Protocol for Preventing Wrong Site, Wrong Procedure, and Wrong Person Surgery™

UP.01.01.01	HAP/CAH	AHC/OBS	BHC	OME	LTC
Conduct a preprocedure verification process.	X	X			
UP.01.02.01					
Mark the procedure site.	X	X			
UP.01.03.01					
A time-out is performed before the procedure.	X	X			

INTERNATIONAL PATIENT SAFETY GOALS (IPSGs)*

Goal 1: Identify Patients Correctly
Standard IPSG.1
The organization develops an approach to improve accuracy of patient identifications.

Goal 2: Improve Effective Communication
Standard IPSG.2
The organization develops an approach to improve the effectiveness of communication among caregivers.

Goal 3: Improve the Safety of High-Alert Medications
Standard IPSG.3
The organization develops an approach to improve the safety of high-alert medications.

Goal 4: Ensure Correct-Site, Correct-Procedure, Correct-Patient Surgery
Standard IPSG.4
The organization develops an approach to ensuring correct-site, correct-procedure, and correct-patient surgery.

Goal 5: Reduce the Risk of Health Care–Associated Infections
Standard IPSG.5
The organization develops an approach to reduce the risk of health care–associated infections.

Goal 6: Reduce the Risk of Patient Harm Resulting from Falls
Standard IPSG.6
The organization develops an approach to reduce the risk of patient harm resulting from falls.

* From *Joint Commission International Accreditation Standards for Hospitals,* 4th Edition

Index